Whole Foods For Whole People

by Lucy Fuller

Published by

TEACH Services, Inc.
Brushton, New York 12916

Copyright © 1994 **TEACH** *Services, Inc.*

ISBN: 0-945383-64-9
LOC: 93-61495

Cover and Divider page Art by
Janine Garner

Published by

TEACH Services, Inc.
Route 1, Box 182
Brushton, New York 12916

Table of Contents

MAIN OBJECTIVES

After a careful study of this book, the reader should be able to:

1. Explain how diet affects ones total well-being.

2. Evaluate and choose the best personal dietary habits.

3. Explain the relationship between a clean blood stream (our river of life) and the following lifestyle principles:

a. Pure air	b. Sunlight
c. Temperance	d. Rest
e. Exercise	f. Proper Diet
g. Use of Water	h. Trust in Divine Power

4. Implement simple, wholesome meal planning, food selection, and preparation in the home setting.

5. Permanently incorporate the principles of proper nutrition:

a. Whole foods	b. Simplicity
c. Palatability	d. Water
e. Regularity	f. Exercise
g. Appetite control	

If you would like a generous supply of current scientific data, supporting the views held in this brief summary on nutrition, you will want the books—"Nutrition for Vegetarians" and "The Animal Connection", by Drs. Agatha and Calvin Thrash of Uchee Pines Institute, 30 Uchee Pines Rd., Seale, AL 36875.

In the preparation of food ~
the golden rays of light
are to be kept shining,
teaching those who sit at the table
how to live
most healthfully.

GENERAL HEALTH PRINCIPLES

LAW AND LIFE—Sickness is a problem and every problem has a cause. No solution to the problem can ever be fully and satisfactorily obtained by dealing with the problem itself, for it is only when the cause is recognized, understood, and removed, that the problem itself will disappear. It will be a brighter day for the human family when the connection between wrong habits of living and the resultant breakdown in health is recognized and steps are taken to remove this universal cause of suffering and death. It is **impossible to indulge every whim of appetite and feeling and at the same time enjoy perfect health and vitality**.

A wise car owner studies his owner's manual carefully and follows its suggestions explicitly. Our Creator has also revealed how our bodies may function at top efficiency. Although the Bible is often relegated to some bygone age, science continues to discover "new" wonders, only to find that the Good Book already had it written down thousands of years ago!

There are definite laws which must be obeyed, and without this discipline, trouble is certain to follow. This may sound restrictive or like an interference with the pleasures of life, but it is not so. The real pleasures of life are in the path of cooperation with the wise and beneficent laws of the Creator, which He wrote in our minds and bodies. As we see the blessings of obedience, we regard it not as a sacrifice but a privilege, as it really is.

God is a Father of infinite love, with whom there is no trace of selfishness. He formulated **laws for our good** as a preserver of the life already given to us and as the means of achieving almost limitless attainments. Violation of those laws brings its own retribution, in the form of various destructive diseases. But while the **broken law is a life-taker**, the **unbroken law is not a life-giver**. Therefore, while the keeping of the law will maintain good health, it cannot restore that which has been destroyed through wrong habits of living.

God alone is the Life-giver. He alone can truly heal sick minds and bodies! **He is just as eager to heal today, as when He walked visibly on earth**. But, God will not work contrary to natural law. If we would be well, we must learn to cooperate with the laws of our being, thus placing ourselves in the **path of inherent blessing**. Thus, we may **open the door** to God's healing power, **allowing** Him to even restore us completely, if He sees this would be best for all concerned.

THE EIGHT NATURAL REMEDIES
(lifestyle medicine)

There are many ways of practicing the healing art; but there is **only one way** that Heaven approves. God's remedies are the **simple** agencies of nature, that will not tax or debilitate the system through their powerful properties. **Pure air, sunlight, temperance, rest, exercise, proper diet, the use of water, trust in divine power**; these are the **true remedies**. Every person should have a knowledge of nature's remedial agencies and how to apply them.

Humans tend to be awe stricken by the physician who seemingly knows how to cure disease. It is far **better**, however, **to know how to prevent illness**, and this we may all do. The beauty of it is, that the basic maintenance and preventive program (with minor alterations), will also reverse or at least stop, the progress of most diseases! It should be the continuing study of every person, how he can more effectively employ these eight simple, yet vital, lifestyle principles or remedies, in his own environment.

Perfect health requires a perfect circulation. In order to have good health, we must have good, free-flowing blood; for the blood is the current of life. It repairs tissues, disposes of wastes, and nourishes the body. When supplied with the proper food elements, and when cleansed and vitalized by contact with pure air, it carries life and vigor to every part of the system. The more perfect the circulation, the better will this work be accomplished.

Let us notice **how** the following eight natural remedies, or laws, if lived out, may promote a **free circulation** of **quality** blood.

1. FRESH AIR

Breathe deeply; few do! Every body cell depends on oxygen for life. Full deep inspirations of pure air which fill the lungs with oxygen, purify the blood. They impart to it a bright color, and send it, a life-giving current, to every part of the body. A good respiration soothes the nerves; it stimulates the appetite and renders digestion more perfect; and it induces sound, refreshing sleep. **Among the first things to be aimed at**, should be a **correct position**, both in sitting and standing. The one who sits and stands erect, is more likely than others to breathe properly.

Outdoor, vital air carries an electrical charge, which is lacking in the indoor, used air. Exercise taken out-of-doors is estimated to be 10 times more beneficial than exercise taken indoors (in a gymnasium or inside the house).

Perfect health requires a perfect circulation; but this cannot be had while three or four times as much clothing is worn upon the body, where the vital organs are situated, as upon the feet and limbs. **It is impossible to have health when the extremities are habitually cold.** In order to secure the most healthful clothing, the needs of every part of the body must be carefully studied. Every article of dress should fit easily, obstructing neither the circulation of the blood nor a free, full, natural respiration.

2. PURE WATER

Daily bathing (outward cleansing) and 6–10 glasses of water (pure as possible) taken internally, dilutes and washes away the poisons and wastes from the body cells, preventing disease. To partake of it freely will assist the excretory organs in eliminating wastes from the blood and daily brings **life-giving, healing power**.

In the summertime, two to three quarts a day may be lost through the skin, by perspiring. Even in the wintertime, up to one quart can be lost through the skin and lungs, without your being aware of it. This fluid must be replaced. If you feel tired and exhausted and your "engine" seems to be running hot, causing you to steam and spout and grumble, check your water level. This may be the problem. Drink enough water to keep the urine pale.

3. SUNLIGHT

Sunlight is one of nature's most healing agents. We may share with vegetation, its life-giving, healing power. There are but few who realize that, in order to enjoy health and cheerfulness, they must have an abundance of sunlight, pure air, and physical exercise. If you would have your homes sweet and inviting, make them bright with air and sunshine. The sunlight may fade your carpets, but it will give a healthy color to the cheeks of your children.

Sunlight has been largely blamed for the incidence of skin cancer, when the main culprit is a faulty diet. Become accustomed to the sunshine gradually. Guard carefully against reddening or burning the skin. Dark-skinned persons require more sunlight than fair-skinned ones, for a therapeutic effect. Studies of children living in slum areas of large cities, where they receive little sunlight (due to smog, tall buildings and narrow alleys), show a much higher incidence of rickets (the sunshine or Vitamin D deficiency disease) in dark-skinned, than in fair-skinned children. So even if the complexion is naturally brown or darker, everyone needs the precious sunlight.

4. PROPER DIET

Good food is the best medicine! **Fruits, nuts, grains, and vegetables** composed God's original diet for man. These are the body's finest building blocks. They contain all the nutrients necessary to make good blood. Millions dig their graves with their teeth. It is in our power to do differently.

Health reform is an intelligent selection of the most healthful articles of food, prepared in healthful, simple ways. God has furnished man with abundant means for the gratification of an un-perverted appetite.

Let the table be made inviting and attractive, as it is supplied with the good things which God has so bountifully bestowed. Let mealtime be a cheerful, happy time. As we enjoy the gifts of God, let us respond by grateful praise to the Giver.

God has given us the fruits, grains and vegetables of the earth for food, that we might have **unfevered blood, calm nerves, and clear minds**. All need to learn that plain, clean living is indispensable to high thinking.

5. EXERCISE

Action is a law of our being. Every organ of the body has its appointed work, upon the performance of which its development and strength depend. Exercise may retard the aging process by several years and will improve one's self-image and mood. **Regular exercise** protects against heart disease by decreasing the triglycerides (a blood fat associated with heart disease), increasing the oxygen intake, lowering the cholesterol and enlarging the blood vessels.

Inactivity is a fruitful cause of disease. Exercise quickens and equalizes the circulation of the blood, but in idleness the blood does not circulate freely, and the changes in it, so necessary to life and health, do not take place. The skin, too, becomes inactive. Impurities are not expelled as they would be, if the circulation had been quickened by vigorous exercise, the skin kept in a healthy condition, and the lungs fed with plenty of pure, fresh air. This state of the system throws a double burden on the excretory organs, and disease is the result.

6. REST

Get a **regular** eight hours (varies a little with individuals) of sleep, nightly. Two hours before midnight, is worth four, after. For best results, go to bed early and arise early! **Too much** sleep is also debilitating.

To those who are brain weary and nervous because of continual labor and close confinement, a visit to the country, where they can live a simple, carefree life, coming in close contact with the things of nature, will be most helpful. Roaming through the fields and the woods, picking the flowers, listening to the songs of the birds, will do far more than any other agency toward their recovery.

More people die for lack of physical exercise, than through over exertion; very many more rust out than wear out. **Exercise neutralizes stress!** It often proves to be the best type of "rest" for the nervous and weary brain worker.

7. TEMPERANCE (Self-control)

Intemperance in almost everything, exists on every hand. People are expending the vital force which they will need at a future time. And when the energy they have so recklessly used, is demanded, they fail for want of it. The physical strength is gone, the mental powers fail.

True temperance teaches us to **dispense entirely** with everything hurtful, and to use **judiciously**, that which is healthful. **There are few who realize** as they should, how much their habits of diet have to do with their health, their character, their usefulness in this world, and their eternal destiny. Sexual intemperance also weakens the mental and physical health, and breaks down the life forces. **Excessive indulgence in anything, is harmful.** True temperance will result in health and happiness.

Something better is the watchword of education, the law of all true living. Whatever God asks us to renounce, He offers in its stead something better.

8. TRUST IN DIVINE POWER

The relation that exists between the mind and the body, is very intimate. When one is affected, the other sympathizes. **Thoughts actually produce various hormones**, which in turn alter the circulation and composition of the blood. Grief, anxiety, discontent, anger, guilt, distrust, jealousy, all tend to break down the life forces and to invite decay and death. On the other hand, courage, gratitude, hope, faith, sympathy, joy and love promote health and prolong life! A contented mind, a cheerful spirit, is health to the body and strength to the soul.

Worry is blind and cannot discern the future; but God sees the end from the beginning. In every difficulty He has His way prepared to bring relief. "No good thing will He withhold from them that walk uprightly." Psalm 84:11. Our heavenly Father invites, "Come unto me, all ye that labor and are heavy laden and I will give you rest." Matthew 11:28.

GENERAL NUTRITIONAL PRINCIPLES

The disease and suffering that everywhere prevail, are largely due to popular errors in regard to diet. By learning to cooperate with the laws of our being, we may avoid much needless suffering and expense.

The cause of nervous breakdown is often believed to be overwork, whereas the actual cause is too much food, eaten at irregular periods, inattention to proper rest and exercise, and often a stimulating lifestyle, that taxes the nervous system. Proper attention to nature's laws can prevent much ill health that is considered to be unavoidable providential outworkings. **Regulating the diet** will do more good than all the hydrotherapy or drug therapy that can be given.

THE TRUE BASIC FOUR FOOD GROUPS—Grains, fruits, nuts, and vegetables constitute the diet chosen for us by our Creator. These foods, prepared in as **simple** and **natural a manner** as possible, are the most healthful and nourishing. They **impart** a **strength**, a **power of endurance**, and a **vigor of intellect**, that are not afforded by a more complex and stimulating diet.

The grains, with fruits, nuts, and vegetables, **contain all the nutritive properties necessary to make good blood**. These elements are not so well or so fully supplied by a flesh diet. Had the use of flesh been essential to health and strength, animal food would have been included in the diet appointed man in the beginning.

DISEASE FROM EXCESS—If we used the standards prepared by the Food and Agriculture Organization, and the World Health Organization, it would be concluded that 70% of the world's population is undernourished. It is strongly suggested by nutrition authorities, that the 30% of the world's population who have an adequate intake are really eating too much. The extra food must be gotten rid of by some mechanism of adaptation, which wears on the body. Certainly, the **high incidence of degenerative diseases**, in those who are "adequately" nourished, indicates that something is seriously wrong with their dietary programs. The **daily requirements** of vitamins, minerals, and protein **have been set far too high, in most instances**. Our emphasis on requirements, has led to the production of much disability and disease, from excessive calories.

Even such a simple thing as how many calories to consume daily, remains an enigma. It has been recommended in this country that Americans consume from 2000 to 2200 calories per day. Note that our population is largely sedentary. By contrast, in Hunza where the people are vigorous and active farmers, being required by circumstances to walk many miles daily, the Hunzakuts use only 1500 to 1735 calories daily. What a difference! And they don't even have to count their calories, because they eat **whole, natural foods**!

AGE OLD RULE STILL WORKS—The best rule to follow is one that has been successfully used for centuries before modern food technology greatly altered our eating habits and the age of degenerative diseases began. **The rule is:** "Eat a wide variety of fruits, vegetables, nuts, and grains. **Get up** from the table **knowing that you could comfortably still eat more." Satisfy hunger, not appetite**. Disease, disability, and early death are much less,. the lower the body weight. Maintain the lowest weight at which your strength is still good. People have lived successfully following this rule for many centuries. We know it works.

THE INTER-DIGESTIVE PHASE of bowel activity is a special **cleansing phase** of the digestive system. Diseases such as inflammations, ulcerations, diverticula and other malfunctions of the intestinal tract, are more likely to afflict one, if the bowel fails to get this cleansing phase after each meal.

The intestinal tract cannot enter this phase of activity unless the stomach and small bowel are free of all food and food residues. Immediately upon completion of moving all food residues from the stomach and small bowel into the colon, the upper gastrointestinal tract slips into the inter-digestive phase. In this special phase, the peristaltic waves are characterized by a different pace and length of activity. The small bowel secretion is different, as are fluid shifts across membrane surfaces.

Many individuals never experience an inter-digestive phase, as they never have an empty bowel. Eating between meals and at irregular meal times forces the bowel to always maintain the digestive phases, and to be deprived of the essential cleaning activity of the inter-digestive phase. A **usual meal requires about four hours** to clear the upper intestinal tract (provided the food is not greasy, and nothing is eaten between meals). Eating or drinking nourishing beverages between meals delays emptying by several hours. Eating at bedtime almost insures that some food will be in the intestinal tract during the night and into the next day, as a reclining position delays digestion even further.

BASIC RULES OF NUTRITION

1. Obtain as **wide a variety of natural (whole, unrefined) foods** as possible. This will give the body an exposure to trace minerals and/or micro nutrients whose existence may not yet be understood.

2. Eat **no refined foods**, **irritating foods** (hot pepper or hot spices), or **fermented or aged products** (cheese, vinegar, spiced pickles, etc.).

3. **Eat only enough to satisfy hunger** (not appetite), **and to maintain an ideal weight.** The "ideal" weight is somewhat below the "normal" usually given on height/weight charts. To enjoy the most vibrant health, consider the following points, as you decide on the needs for the day:

   —Body build and present weight
   —Your age and exercise for the day
   —The climate

4. **Eat on time; nothing between meals.** A lifestyle of strict regularity is strengthening to both mind and body. Have a set time for meals and sleep. Space meals at least five hours apart, and take them in the proper order, quantity-wise; Breakfast 50%, Lunch 40%, and Supper 10%, if any. Nothing, not even juice, should pass the lips **between** meals. Your digestive system needs a complete rest, at times, just as you do!

HOW TO MEET TEMPTATION—Have you found your own promises and resolutions like ropes of sand? Have you come to the end of your rope? There is hope for you! But, **only** through strength from our Creator can we regain our lost self-control. This takes place through a **correct** understanding and use of the **will** (power of choice or deciding power in the nature of man). We should **never** give our mind over to be controlled by another human being (as in the case of hypnotism), but **we may safely do this with an all-powerful, all-knowing, all-loving God!** Many are losers in the battle with appetite (or some other temptation) while hoping and wishing for health and self-control. But they do not come to the point of **yielding the will to God**, and **now choose** to **obey His laws**, as written in their very fibers.

Through the **"right"** exercise of the will, **an entire change may be made in your life!** By yielding up your will to Christ, you ally yourself with the power that is above all principalities and powers. You will have strength from above to hold you steadfast, and thus, **through constant surrender to God**, you will be enabled to live the new life, **even the life of faith. When you believe God** is giving you the victory, **it is even so!**

The human body is wonderfully and fearfully made! Let us show our appreciation for the gift of life, by faithfully caring for this marvelous living machinery. **Choose** just now, to use only the best, simple,l unrefined foods in your dietary. Determine to never again use, even a taste of anything you are convicted is not good for your body. **Complete abstinence from that which is harmful is the only safe rule**, as in the case of the alcoholic. The commission of a known wrong silences the conscience (we go on in indulgence), until the still, small voice becomes so weak that we can no longer tell right from wrong. **Then we cannot reason correctly** about matters that most vitally concern us.

If you should fall back into indulgence, after making a firm decision to do right, don't waste any time "sitting in the mud". Just get right up with the words: **"I choose...and I believe** God will help me". **He will then strengthen your will to do right** as you work with, and not against His laws of nature. When we learn our lesson from the fall, we can **turn defeat into victory** and go on our way with peace and joy in our hearts.

STEPS TO APPETITE AND WEIGHT CONTROL

In order for weight control to be successful, it must represent a **permanent change in lifestyle**. The old lifestyle has been demonstrated to produce overweight, and a change for a few weeks or months, followed by a return to the former lifestyle, will be unsuccessful.

One should learn the difference between appetite and hunger. Appetite is given to us by a loving Creator to help us to enjoy the food which we must have. The basic need of the person, however, is not the enjoyment of food; it is the **need for nutrients.** Appetite should encourage us to supply the **need.** Thoughts of food should not fill the mind. One may properly use appetite to assist in selections to fill the need. The need may be for legumes, whole grains, vegetables, or fruit. Appetite can help one to choose the kind of raw food, the type of grain, or the style of preparation. These needs have been established by the Creator, Who is willing to give us power to fill these needs. Through watchfulness and prayer, one may receive all of his needs, including control of appetite.

1. **Skip 1–2 meals periodically.** Short fasts are a welcome rest to the digestive organs, and an aid in educating the appetite to self-control. It is the best remedy, in many cases of sickness, especially for sedentary or overweight persons.

2. **Eat a hearty breakfast, a good lunch, and little or no evening meal.**

3. **Hunger can be made to be experienced on schedule.** "Correct" sleep gives one more will power. **Be regular** with **sleep, meals, and exercise** schedules.

4. **Not a morsel between meals.** This is a principle of life.

5. **Avoid irritants.** Anything that irritates the stomach or the nervous system acts as a **stimulant to the appetite.** This would include hot spices (mustard, hot pepper, ginger, cloves, nutmeg, cinnamon), caffeinated and decaffeinated drinks, alcohol, baking soda, most baking powders, and all aged, spoiled, or fermented products (aged cheeses, spiced pickles, vinegar, etc.).

6. **Avoid crashes or fads.** Retrain yourself **now**, in a new lifestyle which you can expect to maintain from now on, with only minor variations.

7. **Drink water freely between meals**; enough to keep the urine pale.

8. **Light exercise after meals** promotes digestion. **Never lie down after meals.** This practice slows digestion, promotes hiatal hernias, and could bring on a heart attack in a susceptible individual. A half hour (or even 5 min.) complete relaxation, just **before** the meal is excellent.

9. **Take daily moderate exercise** in the amount of one to five hours. Moderate to heavy exercise suppresses an abnormal appetite.

10. **Use only natural, unrefined foods.** Don't even keep junk foods in the house (all those sweet, rich, oily, fried and highly refined white items)! Put them in the garbage. Junk food will never make good blood!

TIPS FOR THE TABLE

1. Try eating **raw foods first**, or you may not have room for them. If you wish to lose weight, take a large portion of raw foods.

2. Eat only enough to **satisfy hunger, not appetite.**

3. Drink a glass of water a short while **before** the meal. The cause of much stuffing is really thirst.

4. **Learn to relax and enjoy your meal.** Take **smaller bites**, put your fork down between bites and chew your food very thoroughly. It takes about 20 minutes for the satiety center in the brain to register the

14

effects of the first stages of digestion. If you gulp down your food, you may find that you have eaten too much before you feel satisfied.

5. Toward the end of the meal, place the mind resolutely on some pre-planned activity, **not** on the remaining food on the table.

6. When finished, excuse yourself promptly and brush your teeth immediately, to help prevent nibbling.

7. **Pre-plan what you will eat at a restaurant or social gathering**, and stick to the plan. **When traveling, it is best to carry along your own lunch.** (It saves money and health, and may even prevent infection with Aids!)

IF TEMPTED TO EAT BETWEEN MEALS

1. **Drink a glass of cold water.**

2. **Stand erect, breathe deeply, and take a brisk walk**, if possible. Thank God that He is even now giving you back your control over appetite, **as you choose the right.**

3. **Think of how good the next meal will taste** after your stomach has had a proper rest! When you use good whole foods regularly (especially the whole grains), you won't experience so much "hunger" between meals. These foods supply the needs of the system, as impoverished, devitalized foods cannot.

DANGEROUS FOODS

FLESH FOODS—Because of certain serious and life threatening diseases in animals, all animal products carry some risk in their use. Certain of these diseases are so malignant, that many choose to avoid the risk entirely. Luncheon and variety meals, such as salami, sausage, frankfurters, and liverwurst are especially dangerous. They are high in saturated fats. Further, they are often composed of refuse meats that could not be marketed whole because of their disgusting appearance or unwholesome properties. Ground, seasoned, and colored meats are all indications of disguised rejections. If we consume the flesh of an animal, **we have to dispose of the animal's body wastes, as well as our own**, thus placing a double burden on the liver and kidneys.

Animal products are the only source of cholesterol in any diet. However, the use of refined fats causes the body itself, to produce more cholesterol. Therefore the free use of both animal fats and free oils, pose a serious threat to one's health. The high protein content of animal foods causes premature aging. The high fat content tends towards obesity, cancer and diabetes and makes digestion more difficult. With a flesh diet comes also a transfer of stimulating hormones and toxins, that strengthen the animal passions in our nature and weaken the higher centers of the brain. There is no nutritional advantage in using flesh meats, where good, "firsthand" foods are found in abundance. Evidence is mounting that many cancers are caused, not only by pathogens in meat, but by the very nature of animal flesh, and its unsuitability as food for the human digestive system.

DAIRY PRODUCTS AND EGGS—Humans are the only mammals who feel it necessary to continue drinking milk, after being weaned. A virus that causes tumors in cattle has been isolated from commercially available milk, and is NOT inactivated at present pasteurization temperatures. Humans, particularly children, often drink milk that contains a virus which has been proven to induce leukemia in cattle and chimpanzees and can infect human cells. Anyone who has worked around the poultry industry, knows of the high incidence of malignant growths in chickens. As disease increases in the animal kingdom, there will be less and less safety in using any animal products. If used at all, milk or eggs should come from healthy animals, and should be well sterilized (not just pasteurized). Raw milk may be a little more nutritious, but is it worth the risk? These foods are high in cholesterol, protein and fat and should be used sparingly, if used at all, rather than as staples. When large amounts of dairy products are used, we see an earlier onset of puberty and an earlier aging pattern.

IRRITATING SUBSTANCES—break down the delicate mucus membranes of the gastrointestinal tract, causing nervousness, unnatural cravings, and even bleeding ulcers!

1. **Hot spices and seasonings.** Simple rule: Avoid anything that feels hot to the tongue, when not heated on the stove; black, white and red, hot pepper, horse radish, cloves, cinnamon, ginger, mustard, nutmeg, and Hungarian paprika. (See list of safe seasonings in the "Recipe" section of this book.)

2. **All caffeinated drinks:** Coca Cola, most soft drinks, coffee, tea, etc. Decaffeinated coffee should also be avoided, as it contains more caffeol, a bladder irritant, than the regular coffee.

3. **Chocolate in all its forms.** Theobromine and caffeine, the main toxic alkaloids in chocolate, can cause central nervous system stimulation, sleeplessness, hyperactivity, itching, depression, breast nodules and anxiety. Carob is a healthful and delicious substitute for chocolate. It is best to use only the pure carob powder, in any preparation you may make. The commercial candy bars, chips and coated items are loaded with refined oils, sweetening, etc.

4. **All products that pass through a fermenting, putrefying or aging process:** All hard or aged cheeses (these contain very toxic substances due to fermentation and molds), vinegar, or foods containing it, alcohol, pickles, fermented soy sauce ("La Choy" has one that is not fermented), spoiled fruit, etc.

5. **Baking Soda and Baking powders**—Baking soda and **most** baking powders either harm nutrients in the food or leave irritating residues in the system. Yeast raised breads are healthful, provided the bread is well baked and then not consumed until the 2nd or 3rd day. **Fresh** yeast germs retard digestion and harm some of the B vitamin content of the product. Aluminum (found in some baking powders, antacids, some deodorants, artificial flavorings, etc., and **especially** in aluminum canned soft drinks) may be a cause of Alzheimer's disease, so we would do well to avoid these products.

   We have discovered two quick leavening agents which we feel would be safe for occasional use. These are: *Ener-G* baking powder (calcium and citric acid) or 3% hydrogen peroxide. They are discussed under **"Special Terms and Ingredients"**.

6. **Excess concentrated natural foods:** Honey, salt, nuts, dried fruit or even fruit juices should be used sparingly, as one can easily overeat of these. It is best to use the whole fruit or vegetable, as a rule, rather than juices. If it is needed in the case of illness, the juice should be **used as the meal**, and not be taken at all hours. This starts the whole digestive process going again and delays recovery. If used with a regular meal, just a small glass of juice would be best.

IMPOVERISHED FOODS—SLOW KILLERS

We don't like to speak of negative factors, but it's high time to let people know that the free use of refined fractionated foods, results in the varied degenerative diseases and premature aging that plague society today. Some commonly used refined foods are: White flour, pasta and degerminated cornmeal and all products made from these items; alcoholic drinks, pop and Kool-Aid drinks; sugar, grease and oil of all kinds and all products containing these items. Grease of any kind is especially harmful, as it greatly retards digestion and causes abnormalities in the blood circulation and cell metabolism. Following are listed some of the physiological effects from the use of refined or impoverished foods:

1. Malnutrition

2. Lower phagocytic index (destroys our ability to fight disease)

3. Hypoxia—Decreased oxygen in the tissues, a base cause of most diseases

4. Digestive tract disorders (constipation, hemorrhoids, diverticulitis, cancer of the colon, etc.)

5. Blood sugar problems (diabetes, hypoglycemia)

6. Liver and kidney diseases

7. Osteoporosis—high protein diet, and lack of exercise and sunlight, causing leaching of the bone minerals

8. Cancer, heart disease, arthritis and other diseases

9. Shortened life span and poor quality of life

10. Poor memory, depression, chronic fatigue, and allergies

REFINED CARBOHYDRATES (starches and sugars)—Carbohydrates provide for, by far, the largest share of our daily energy needs. Most people are aware that white sugar and flour are not best for one. **But most are not** aware of the **large percentage of refined grain products** they are consuming in the form of prepared cereals, pastas, white rice, sweet breads and crackers! Please read labels before buying. A handful of whole wheat flour, a little wheat germ, a few flakes of bran, and a fine "country sounding" name, don't make up for all the nutrients that have been removed from these impoverished foods! Bread and potatoes are often blamed for putting excess weight on people, when the real culprits are the refined fats and sugars that are **added** to these foods.

It is virtually impossible to buy good, **100% whole grain breads**, without a generous dose of **grease, sugar, and preservatives.** We recommend that you learn to make your own breads and cereals, from whole grains. There are some simple recipes available. Your efforts will be repaid with increased vigor, better dispositions, and more money in your pocket (instead of the doctor's)! Do not buy anything with preservatives like potassium bromate, which chemically ages the product. The commercial breads with more whole grain flour in them, **also contain more preservatives** than white bread, as a rule. So, the best way to win, is to make good homemade bread. It smells so good when baking, and tastes great too! See our recipe section for some good, simple recipes. We recommend **"Basic Whole Wheat Bread"** for a starter.

REFINED FATS (liquid or solid)—Oils or fats are handled by the digestive tract in a different manner than other nutrients, being emulsified in the duodenum (first part of the small intestine) and taken up mainly in the lymphatic vessels (rather than the blood vessels). The lymphatic vessels form a one way system from the intestines to a large blood vessel in the chest, which in turn dumps its contents right into the main blood stream.

The fluid in the lymphatic vessels is milky after an average American meal, due to the emulsified fat present. **This free fat causes our red blood cells to stick or clump together**, thus clogging small blood vessels and **causing hypoxia (lack of oxygen) in tissues** beyond that point. **Low oxygen in the tissues is a basic cause of all the degenerative diseases we see everywhere. Both refined fats and refined sugars, destroy our immune system,** by paralyzing our white blood cells, and causing a sluggish circulation of the blood.

Our bodies need fats, but only as nature presents them (encased in cells and combined with other nutrients), **versus** in a refined, concentrated state. For example, not many of us would sit down and eat 12 large ears of corn at one sitting, but it takes that many ears to make just one level tablespoon of oil! **The free use of oils of all kinds, is a real problem in the diet.** Because of the coating action of free fats (especially when heated, as in fried foods), they **greatly retard digestion**. The food then has time to ferment and **the body has to live on decayed, fermented matter**. There are an abundance of natural fats in grains, fruits, vegetables, and nuts (the latter should be used sparingly, as their hard shells would indicate)! These fats come intact, with the vitamins and other nutrients which aid in their metabolism, and prevent them from turning rancid, once inside the warm body environment.

REFINED PROTEIN—It is usually assumed that a high protein diet is entirely harmless. That this is **not** true, is well attested to by both animal experimentation and population studies. Reports in prominent medical journals of the dangers of high protein feedings have been largely overlooked, until very recent times. **Animals' lives are shortened considerably by a diet containing liberal quantities of protein.** Diets containing around 10% of the calories in the form of protein seem to be the best, in regard to the quality of health and life span. As the amount of protein increases, maturation is faster, and the life span is shorter. Further, the kidneys may enlarge up to 50% larger than in animals on normal or "low" protein diets. Most animals develop **kidney disease** while on prolonged high protein intake; **many also develop cancers**.

It is definite that the human body is overworked in converting protein into energy, and the process may involve real danger. **Complex carbohydrates** (whole grains, vegetables, legumes and fruits) **are the most efficient energy foods, regardless of popular notions to the contrary**. To use protein for fuel, is also an expensive process, since the cost of high protein foods (meat, dairy products or refined vegetable protein meat analogs) generally runs much higher than complex carbohydrate foods. **Athletes show greater energy and endurance on high carbohydrate diets.** To consume about 75% of our calories as complex carbohydrates, appears to promote the best functioning of all parts of the living machinery.

Instead of extracting pure protein from plant foods, or using the flesh of animals, **why not use unrefined, firsthand plant foods, which contain just the right proportions of proteins, fats, and carbohydrates**? Thus we may avoid the dangers of a high protein diet, and yet obtain an abundance of high quality protein.

REFINED VITAMINS AND MINERALS—Today we are being bombarded with the idea that everyone needs vitamin and mineral supplements, and that large doses are good for the cure or prevention of diseases like the cold, arthritis, heart disease, and even cancer. It used to be only the food faddists who advocated a free use of these potent, concentrated and refined nutrients. Now the voices of many highly respected professionals have joined them. It is a multi-million dollar industry, to be sure, but who wants to be a guinea pig? When God created all things, (including natural foods), He said, **"And behold it was very good"**. Fruits, nuts, grains and vegetables still contain all the elements of nutrition. When man tampers with his food, as with any other natural resource, he always ends up with an imbalanced situation! The following ideas and scientific findings, from several prevention oriented medical doctors, may be of help to some, in getting back to the simple dietary plan given man in the beginning.

Do we need vitamin and mineral supplements? Maybe Yes—if we are eating an average American diet (refined and devitalized). Maybe yes, **when** even eating a vegetarian diet with lots of refined meat substitutes, polyunsaturated oils and refined grains. **As a rule, no**—if we are eating a diet with a variety of fruits, whole grains, legumes, nuts, and properly prepared vegetables (grown on different soils). There are abnormal conditions which call for some of these concentrated nutrients, but this is the exception, not the rule.

Dr. Mervyn G. Hardinge, a long-time professor of physiology at Loma Linda University, in California, tells us that **no one really knows how much we need** of each of these micro nutrient. An overdose of one nutrient may cause deficiency symptoms of another. And what about the nutrients we haven't discovered yet? What about the vitamin pill—how old is it? How potent is it? What about deteriorated substance in old vitamin pills—are they toxic? A multivitamin capsule will usually include more of the cheap vitamins, less of the expensive ones.

Animal studies and human observations (in a Philippine concentration camp, during World War II) reveal that **deficiency signs appeared sooner** in the animals/humans who had been receiving supplements, before the vitamin was withheld. The **body became wasteful in its use of the vitamin**, when there was an excess around. If now, in a time of plenty, we must rely on these supplements to keep us healthy, what will we do when hard times come, and no supplements are available? Who will develop the deficiencies first?

Let's look at the **dietary of people who have excellent health,** no cardiovascular atherosclerotic disease, diabetes or hypertension. The Tarahumara Indians of Mexico are known for their phenomenal feats of endurance: walking 100 miles in 5 days; Kickball games of 100 miles in 2 days; carrying heavy burdens (100 pound sack) for 100 miles in 70 hours. They are on an approximately 80% carbohydrate–10% fat–10% protein diet (or food as grown). A variety of grains and vegetables with some fruit and nuts, makes up the diet—no supplements.

We will discuss vitamin B_{12} in particular, as many would-be vegetarians are quite concerned over reports on how one may not be able to obtain enough of this vitamin, on a pure vegetarian diet. Since the body does not "burn up" or "wear out" Vitamin B_{12}, we need only to replace what little is lost in the bile and not reabsorbed (only about 0.5 microgram per day). There is sound evidence that pernicious anemia (a B_{12} deficiency disease) arises, **not from a** shortage of B_{12} in the diet, **but from impairment of the ability to absorb** the vitamin. A high protein and fat diet (the average American fare) and large doses of vitamin C have been shown to increase the body requirement for Vitamins B_{12} and B_6. According to Dr. Mervyn Hardinge, there are three non-animal sources of Vitamin B_{12}, discovered to date. It is synthesized by micro organisms a) on the teeth and other sites in the oral cavity, b) a small amount is absorbed from the lower intestine, c) is found in most drinking water (chlorine does not seem to affect it).

There are vast populations in Africa, in Southeast Asia, in India, who are vegetarians by necessity, and they have no vitamin B_{12} deficiencies. Vitamin B_{12} deficiencies are seen in people on the refined, supplemented western diet. It is becoming more and more evident that a person eating a natural diet, high in fiber and complex carbohydrates and low in fat, protein and refined foods, needs **less** B_{12} and many of the other micro nutrients, than the meat eater, or the vegetarian who uses concentrated, refined meat substitutes and polyunsaturated oils freely.

What about minerals? Breast-fed babies almost never have trace mineral deficiencies. The colostrum, or first breast secretion, is the richest in these minerals, and their level decreases in the milk as the lactation period continues. So the breast-fed baby has a head start on trace minerals.

Better transportation has made it possible to obtain foods from various locations. While the soil in one area may be deficient in a certain mineral, food grown in another locality will make up the lack. It is rare that a person would eat grains, vegetables and fruits, all from the same area. If the **soil** is properly "fed" and prepared, this should hold no drawback. Sea salt, kelp and seaweeds, when available, may be a good natural food source of trace minerals, if you feel the need of more than you can obtain from other more common foods.

The minerals in particular must be in balance. Minerals that we need in small amounts for health, such as copper, zinc, iron, chromium and manganese, etc., are antagonists to each other. When one ingests a large amount of one, it can depress another mineral, possibly causing deficiency symptoms. This will never happen when using an abundance of natural foods, as grown; but can occur when concentrated supplements are used. It would be best to correct the faulty lifestyle, rather than to take concentrated nutrients, whose full effect we do not know.

Causes of Vitamin/Mineral loses or malabsorption:

1. **Lack of exercise, a high protein diet, and lack of sunlight will cause the bones to lose calcium,** especially if the protein is meat (due to the high sulfur content of meat). Then the bones become brittle and break easily (osteoporosis).

2. **Improper Cooking.** The use of baking powder and soda, in baked goods or in the preparation of vegetables, destroys vitamins, and irritates the stomach lining. The water in which vegetables, legumes, etc. are cooked, contains vitamins and should not be discarded.

3. **Drugs and other foreign substances.** For example, the "pill" increases the need for vitamin C; alcohol consumption calls for more B_1, B_6, and folic acid; antibiotics destroy the intestinal bacterial flora, which synthesize vitamins K, B_1, folacin, and B_{12}, so these will be in low supply; mineral oil, taken internally, dissolves fat soluble vitamins, but is indigestible, so it carries vitamins out of the system when it is passed. Most drugs are irritating to the digestive tract, causing it to be unhealthy and unable to absorb nutrients properly.

4. **Refined or "Enriched" foods.** The more concentrated protein (meat or meat substitutes) consumed, the more B_6, B_{12}, B_1, etc., needed to metabolize these items. The more oil or fat of any kind consumed, the more Vitamin E is required to keep this oil from turning rancid in our tissues and damaging cells (premature aging and death of cells). If we would learn to eat only natural foods (as grown), we would get plenty of vitamin E and other antioxidants to protect the polyunsaturated oils, naturally present in the food. So-called "enriched" foods are misleading. They may have 20% of the nutrients removed and only 5% added back, yet they are called enriched! The iron and calcium, etc., which are added to refined foods, have another problem. They are not as assimilable (usable) in the body as are the minerals naturally present in food as grown. The American Heart Association recently went on record to say that excessive iron enrichment of foods ranks second only to smoking, as the strongest risk factor for heart disease and heart attacks!

5. **Lack of Sunlight.** Sunlight is one of nature's most healing agencies. The best way to get Vitamin D is from the sunshine. **Sunlight converts our own body cholesterol into Vitamin D. The body will never produce a toxic level of this vitamin.** Many of the fat soluble vitamins are known to be toxic when taken in large doses. Ingested Vitamin D has been shown to be toxic to the smooth muscle in the blood vessels, causing destruction, thereby setting the stage for arteriosclerosis and atherosclerosis (heart disease). Some authorities are calling for the elimination of all Vitamin D supplementation of milk and cereal products. But dairymen fear they would lose many sales, if they were to omit this additive.

6. **Stress alters the motility of the gastrointestinal tract, reduces production** of digestive **enzymes, and reduces absorption** from the digestive tract. Stress may also cause an **increase in the bowel metabolic rate**, causing an increase in the need for vitamins. Those who are excited, anxious, or in a hurry, would do well not to eat until they have found rest or relief; for the vital powers, already severely taxed, cannot supply the necessary digestive fluids.

7. **Certain diseases** may also prevent vitamins from being absorbed well, as in the case of: sprue, celiac disease, ulcerative colitis, Crohn's disease, some parasitic infections (notably giardiasis), peptic ulcer, etc.

8. **Multiple Food Combinations at one meal.** Because of the physical or chemical interactions, many nutrients compete with one another for absorption sites, or are absorbed or attached in such a way as to be unavailable for utilization or absorption. **Simple** menus, delightfully served, provide the greatest endurance and sense of well-being.

9. **Poor Chewing.** The chemicals of digestion do not have ready access to all parts if the food is delivered to the stomach in chunks. Food should be chewed to a cream in the mouth before it is swallowed. If your time to eat is limited, do not bolt your food down, but eat less, and masticate thoroughly. The benefit derived from food does not depend so much on the quantity eaten, as on its thorough digestion; nor the gratification of taste so much on the amount of food swallowed, as on the length of time it remains in the mouth.

Some, out of ignorance, have been relying on vitamin/mineral supplements. Others find it easier to pop a pill or two daily, than to put forth the effort to exercise, obtain plenty of sunlight and pure water, or to learn to prepare food properly. Anything worthwhile in life, takes effort and perseverance, but in the long run, good health habits make life much easier and more satisfying. There is a cause and effect relationship in everything we do: breathe, eat, drink, exercise, and think, etc. Disease never comes without a cause.

We should nourish our body tissues with good vitamins and minerals, by eating an abundance of fruits, whole grain products, legumes and vegetables and a moderate use of nuts and seeds. It is cheaper and much more healthful to obtain our vitamins an minerals from the garden or grocery store than from a "pill shop". Can you see what we are doing to ourselves? By the ingestion of refined, processed, imbalanced food, by smoking, drinking, using powerful drugs, we are creating an ideal situation for a vitamin and/or mineral deficiency. We have created the market for the multi-million dollar supplementation business!

DIETARY FIBER—The following are a few summary thoughts from a lecture given by Dr. Dennis P. Burkitt, and published in the 1983 spring issue of The Journal of Heath and Healing, PO Box 109, Wildwood, GA 30757. Doctor Burkitt is an honorary senior research fellow of St. Thomas Medical School, London.

The size of a hospital required for any given community will be directly proportionate to the size of the stools which the population passes. The average American passes from 2½–4 oz. of stool a day; a mere 2 oz. in the elderly. In the third world they pass 1–1½ lb. per day! And this is highly important. In these less mechanized, sophisticated nations, the degenerative diseases (cancer, arthritis, heart disease, diverticulitis, diabetes, appendicitis, obesity, and constipation, etc.) are almost nonexistent!

Colon cancer incidence is directly related to the transit time (time it takes the food you eat to be passed in the stool). A bulky stool will pass easily out of the colon, (as toothpaste will from a **full** tube of paste). It is the pentose fraction of dietary fiber that has the most profound effect on the stool size. Pentoses are highest in **unrefined cereal foods** (bread, dry and soft cooked cereals, crackers, etc.). That is why we put maximum emphasis on **unrefined cereals**. Potatoes are also an excellent food if they don't come near grease in the preparation, or in the eating of them. **One loaf of good whole grain bread** bulks your stool equivalent to **eight loaves of white bread**!

Fiber also lowers the blood cholesterol. Your chance of a long and healthy life are more closely related to your stool output than to your serum cholesterol level, blood pressure, glucose tolerance curve, or the other things the laboratories measure. We've got to get down to what causes disease in the first place!

Try to picture a room with water flowing from a faucet, overflowing from the basin and flooding the floor. Two gentlemen are faced with the problem of keeping the floor dry. They decide to spend 18 hours a day mopping the floor, to get better and better mops, pails and sponges etc. But it never seems to occur to them that it might be better to turn off the faucet! The faucet stands for the real causes of sickness, the moppers represent the average doctors, hospitals and all that goes with them. The moppers are much more successful financially, than the faucet turners, for **preventive medicine** teaches people how to get well, and stay well, through simple and inexpensive means, within the reach of all. Dr. Burkitt confesses that he too, was a contented mopper and took many mopping courses (which have their place in caring for certain emergencies). He is now a happy faucet turner, and urges other physicians to join the team! In this proud "scientific" age, we need to be careful that we don't become eligible for the comment from poet Ogden Nash, "We are making great progress, but we are heading in the wrong direction."

HEALTH BUILDING PROGRAM

Study carefully, the **"Eight Natural Remedies"** section in the foregoing pages of this book. Seek at once to incorporate these principles of life, into your daily program, to the best of your ability. Study the page on **"Dietary Fiber"** and take appropriate measures to correct any lack of proper bowel elimination. A person with a clogged colon is like a city or house with a backed up sewer system. Some symptoms of this condition are: bad breath, a sluggish or melancholic attitude, a full feeling in the abdomen and minor skin eruptions such as pimples. A complete switch to a whole foods diet (food as grown), along with an increase in daily outdoor exercise and water intake, will soon show a marked improvement in bowel problems.

A change in diet takes education and determination. The appetite for food is the strongest passion with which man has to deal. If the appetite is **rightly** educated (to use only that which is beneficial to the body),, it will soon learn to relish simple, wholesome food, even **more** than it used to enjoy the hurtful dainties. Give it a fair try, and you'll find such an improvement in mental, physical and spiritual health, that you won't want to return to the "old way." Temptations to indulgence are found everywhere, but there is a way to meet these successfully. (Please see the suggestions on how one may become a master, rather than a slave, to appetite in the section, **"How to Meet Temptation"**.)

The Recommended Diet Plan

1. **Fast for one day** (omit this fast if you are hypoglycemic or diabetic). Eat nothing with calories during this time, but drink plenty of water; un-sweetened tea would be fine, for something warm to drink. Spend as much time out-of-doors as possible, and exercise as your strength will permit.

2. **Use a grain/vegetable diet for 2–4 weeks.** Prepare raw and steamed vegetables (be sure to include plenty of dark greens, such as collards or kale, and fresh, raw vegetables of all kinds) and cooked or baked natural brown rice or millet. These two whole grains have been chosen, because they contain no gluten, to which many persons are allergic. Vegetables, rather than fruits are stressed, because a large majority of sufferers have blood sugar level imbalances. The use of only vegetables (which are low in natural sugars), gives a "sick" pancreas a chance to rejuvenate. Lemon juice and tomato (for salads), along with a **little** salt, herbs or vegetable seasonings, may be used as taste enhancers (omit all salt for a while, if blood pressure is elevated). A glass of fresh carrot juice or green drink, taken 15 minutes before the meal, will give you an additional boost in rebuilding your health. Garlic, onions and parsley are great health promoting foods. Onions and parsley may be used generously, in salads. Learn to cook greens, potatoes, even rice, with plenty of onion and garlic. They are mild when cooked, but add a rich flavor. Eat only 2 or 3 meals per day, at set times, at least 5 hours apart, including no more than 4 varieties at any one meal, and take **nothing** between meals but water. Train yourself to eat a good breakfast and a light evening meal, so that the whole body may rest during the sleep period.

3. After the short fast and the vegetable/rice diet phase, you may **add fruits of all kinds** (omit dried fruits, very sweet fruits and honey, if you are a diabetic or severe hypoglycemic), legumes (beans, peas and lentils), other whole grains, and nuts, seeds (used sparingly, as a creamer in gravies, soup, dressings, etc.). For desserts, it is best to use sweet fresh fruit, or desserts sweetened with dried fruit, fruit juices, or juice concentrate, or a **little** honey or *Sucanat*.

You will need to make your own bread and cereal products unless you can find a bakery that will bake bread with 100% whole grain flour and will leave out grease or oil and sugar. It is **best** not to take fruit and vegetables at the same meal, as vegetables take longer to digest, than fruit. There are some fruit/vegetables that seem to go either way, such as tomatoes, hard winter squash, melons and pineapple (which is actually the swollen stem of a plant). We **do not** recommend any complicated food combination chart. Experience will show individuals, which foods go nicely together. Food and diet matters should not fill the mind. Let us eat for strength, and **rejoice** in the health and strength we **now** possess, **as** we work toward something better!

4. **If You Want to Lose Weight More Rapidly**—Omit all seeds, nuts, and olives for several weeks. But you may eat freely of whole grain breads and cereals, fruits and vegetables and legumes. Bread, potatoes and bananas are often blamed for putting on excess weight, when the real culprit is all the grease, oil and sugars that are added to these foods! Please read the section in this book on **"Steps to Weight Control"**. Vigorous exercise decreases the appetite cravings, and adds zest to the spirits. Tasty salad dressings may be made in an electric blender, from tomatoes, and/or rice, lemon and vegetable seasonings (see recipe for **"Tomato French Dressing"**). Whole grain corn bread, steaming hot, nicely seasoned pinto beans and a large green salad, make a satisfying meal, while still allowing you to lose weight. A natural whole foods diet allows for gradual weight loss, which **best** preserves proper skin tone, or turgor. **Whole grain breads and cereals** should be the staple food in both the **"Weight Loss"**, and basic **"Health Building"** diets. They are loaded with vitamins and minerals, as well as good fiber, which keeps the system "swept out" properly.

Miscellaneous Guidelines

1. Serve two or three meals **on schedule**, with **nothing** between meals, not even a peanut or fruit juice! The pernicious habit of snacking lays the foundation for disease, for the digestive system is the foundation of life and health. In order to retain a healthy tone, it **must** have a **complete rest period**, after all food has passed from the small bowel. This necessitates at least a 5–hour period between meals. If they have courage to try it, most would experience better health and see digestive disorders disappear, if they would accustom themselves to only two meals per day.

2. Learn to drink enough water to keep the urine pale and nearly odorless. When a person keeps himself well hydrated, the irritation that calls for so much water at mealtimes, will disappear. Much liquid taken with the meal, delays digestion and dilutes digestive enzymes.

3. Take sun baths at least twice a week. Take only sub-erythema doses (not enough to redden the skin). Please reread the section on "Sunlight". Expose as much of the body as possible (find a secluded spot). Sunlight is very healing and relaxing. A dark-skinned person needs more sunlight, for a therapeutic effect, than a fair-skinned one. Sunlight has come to be feared, but what is the real reason for this? If you are using no refined fats or oils (which turn rancid in the tissues and damage the cell membranes and organelles, due to their lack of antioxidants), the sun is a wonderful healing agent and not a cancer threat (when used in sub-reddening doses!).

4. We will re-emphasize the fact that proper regulation of the diet will do more in recovering and maintaining health, than all the medicines or water treatments, etc., in the world! The science of preparing simple, tasty and healthful meals takes study and practice, like **anything** else **important in life.** We can guarantee that efforts in implementing God's 8 natural lifestyle principles or remedies, will be well repaid. Once you have regained your health, you will want to stay on the program, with minor variations, in order to stay well. We hope you will pass on this vital information to others, who are longing for better health, and want to know how they can cooperate with natural law.

GARDENING AND FOOD PRESERVATION

Raise as much of your own food as possible. The importance of a home garden cannot be overestimated. With economic problems ever on the increase, a good garden may make the difference between hunger and a well supplied table! Even if one has a good income, gardening provides valuable exercise, satisfaction, and is a real soother of the nerves. The garden is the best schoolroom for young children. If a love for this type of work is cultivated early, it would save many youth from a downward course. The sick, also, find health and happy thoughts, in the garden. **No one succeeds in gardening without giving attention to the natural laws involved.** Each plant requires different care. Even the work itself is a blessing, as it develops character traits, which help in our everyday life and contact with others. **When the soil has been properly worked and nourished, the plants will be healthy and better able to resist disease and pests.** It it wonderful to be able to pick fresh produce and small fruits from the garden!

Much expense can be saved by canning, drying, or freezing fruits and vegetables, when in season. Preserve most of the items you like to use most frequently (such as tomatoes and apples). Home canned applesauce, from good, ripe apples, is much more flavorful than the un-sweetened variety in the grocery store! Some neighbor or friend would be happy to share their knowledge of food preservation with you. Do not, however, waste time or freezer and jar space, with sugar-filled jams and jellies. There are easy-to-make recipes for natural jams and fruit butters (see our recipes). Following, is a list of some helpful home canning equipment you may want to obtain.

> 1 or 2 Sauce Pots, large stainless steel (for hot-pack method of canning)
> Water bath Canner (for quart jars, or ½ gallon, according to your needs)
> Jars, Lids, and Rings (glass is preferred to tin for canning)
> Jar Filler, sturdy and wide-rimmed
> Cup dipper with a Spout, one quart size (for filling jars, using the hot-pack method)
> Dishpans, two large and several small
> Utility Pans, 1 to 3
> Pressure Cooker Canner, large (for canning vegetables, and cooking dry beans)

GENERAL FOOD PREPARATION

Cooking with unrefined plant foods (versus refined or secondhand products) does require a change in food preparation habits, but it need not require more time altogether. The key to successfully preparing whole foods, with a minimum of time being involved, centers on some basic points of organization. The following suggestions are some key points to keep in mind.

KITCHEN SETUP

In the kitchen, one's possessions and equipment should not exceed the storage space available. A clean kitchen, with a place for everything, will go far toward making a happy home. Store all basic ingredients (grains, flours, dry legumes, nuts, seeds, etc.) in reasonable quantities, within easy-as-possible reach of the work area. Flour, meal, or shelled nuts should be stored in the refrigerator or freezer, especially in humid hot climates.

UTENSILS AND APPLIANCES

1. **Measuring Equipment.** For dry ingredients, use nested measuring cups (a cup for each fraction of a cup). For liquid measuring, obtain one-cup, two-cup, and possibly four-cup sized glass measuring cups. Use the size of cup closest to the amount to be measured, for the greatest accuracy and ease.

2. **Chopping Equipment.** Vegetables, nuts, and fruits do require cutting or chopping at times. Therefore, it is best to have a large, straight edge knife designed for chopping, as well as several good paring knives. Purchase a good knife sharpener. Use it, and your work will be much easier. A nut chopper of some kind is helpful, also.

3. **Blending or Grinding Equipment.** A blender is an extremely versatile machine and expands the possibilities for creative cooking. **A good blender** need not be very expensive, **but should be durable enough to meet the demands placed on it**. Be sure **not to overload it**, and use a **supple** rubber spatula to clean down the sides while blending or removing a mixture from the blender. A glass top will stand heat the best. The **Moulinex Coffee grinder** (or mini blend jar by **Osterizer**), **helps you stretch nuts,** used in baking special breadstuffs or in making milks, creams, sauces, spreads, etc. By grinding them finely, the flavor of the nuts blends more evenly with the product, requiring fewer nuts for the same taste effect. An electric hand beater makes a good inexpensive bread-making machine. Use it to develop the gluten at the batter stage.

4. **Cooking and Baking Equipment.** A pressure cooker is easy to use and serves its purpose well for cooking beans, grains, and vegetables. Several sauce pans with tight fitting lids and a steaming rack or basket, are also indispensable aids in cooking vegetables for maximum nutrient retention. Nonstick bakeware and skillet are very helpful in baking whole grain breadstuffs.

5. **Miscellaneous Equipment.** For nourishing lunches, at least **one wide-mouth thermos bottle for each person regularly carrying a lunch is very helpful**. A **nonstick waffle iron** makes a nice addition to cereal possibilities. Waffles may also be used with fruit as a waffle cake (stack) or dried and toasted in the oven as zwieback. An **oven thermometer** will help you know for sure what temperature your oven registers. A **minute timer** gives you freedom to do something else, while an item is baking, without risk of burning it.

COOKING HABITS

1. Planning ahead will save time and prevent much frustration.

   a. A simple menu planner sheet, with a section for a daily work memo, prevents going over the same plans and decisions, several times. See our menu planner sheet. You may like a different format, so feel free to change it around to suit your needs.

   b. Soaking legumes, a waffle mix, etc., will shorten cooking time. In the case of waffles, soaking makes a lighter end product.

   c. Breadstuffs, simple casseroles or sandwich spreads may be prepared ahead and frozen, for quick serving. Beans of different kinds may be pressure-canned in Mason jars for later use.

2. **Don't Overbuy or Underbuy.** This will cause spoilage or waste of time and gasoline. Make a list of supplies and groceries. When an item runs low, place it on the shopping list at once. Simple dishes make it easier to use leftovers and still make them palatable and uncomplicated.

3. **Health Habits.** You must take care of the "homemaker", if she is to continue serving tasty nutritious meals. So, take yourself in hand. Wear comfortable shoes and clothing. Alternate sitting and standing (especially during canning season). Learn to sit and stand correctly, and you will avoid fatigue due to poor posture. Do not think a short nap before dinner is a waste of time, for it can help you enjoy the last hours of the day's work. Daily, vigorous **outdoor** exercise is a must!

4. How to Make a Recipe Turn Out Right.

   a. Read the recipe carefully.

   b. Before you begin mixing, do whatever special job needs to be done, such as chopping nuts, etc.

   c. Get ingredients together on counter. Collect utensils.

   d. Turn heat to correct temperature, if preheated oven is needed.

   e. Measure exactly. It often makes a difference.

   f. Follow every step exactly as directed.

   g. Bake or cook as directed.

   h. Cool, serve, or store as directed.

PREPARATION OF WHOLE GRAINS

THE MOST IMPORTANT FOOD—Grains represent the most important single item in the dietary. For many nations, grains in some form represent the main dish at all meals. We can expect that eating **whole** grains will bring a better disposition, greater ambition, increased ability to successful work production, and greater ability to experience happiness. With all of these benefits, it is important to carefully examine the grains and study how they can best be used in our menus.

TWO MISTAKES—Two mistakes are often made in connection with grains: the **refining** (polishing), and the **failure to cook a sufficient length of time**. Grains are packaged in such a way that the vitamins and minerals are carried almost entirely on the outer layer. Milling generally removes this layer leaving a white, easily ground, central kernel, which is almost devoid of vitamins and minerals. The central portion contains the starch and the protein, but both of these are more difficult to metabolize without the accompanying minerals, vitamins and fiber. **The B vitamins are required in the metabolism of starches and sugars.** Many of the minerals are required in the metabolism of protein. We can easily see that whole grains are made-to-order. When used in the refined state, they become much less efficient in the body metabolism. Bleaching is another "thief" of the vitamins and minerals in the grain. When the flour or grain product is labeled "Enriched", the case is not much better. **Only a fraction of some** of the lost nutrients are returned to the refined product. It is as though someone were to steal $20 from you, and then return $5, and call you enriched!

Many people fail to cook or bake grains long enough to release the chemical bonds between the small units of the molecules. Our digestion is not strong enough to entirely split many molecules in grains, thereby causing us to suffer some distress in the colon, to form gas, or to fail to receive all the benefits possible from the whole grains. The harder, whole kernel cereals, require several hours slow cooking. Rolled oats and bulgur wheat have been partially cooked, and require less cooking. Finely ground cornmeal, requires less cooking time than course grits or cracked wheat, etc. Dextrinizing grain (lightly browning in oven or dry skillet) adds a nice flavor variation and greatly shortens the cooking time.

THE REAL STAFF OF LIFE—There are a number of grains, each having individual chemical characteristics and flavor qualities, that make a whole new set of eating experiences with each grain. Rice, for instance, can be cooked out dry and used with a number of sauces, spreads, gravies, and soups. By simply increasing the cooking time and the water, the end product is creamy, and can be used as porridge for breakfast (with or without dried fruit); can be chilled in a mold, sliced and browned in the oven; or may be shaped while still hot, into patties, after seasoning it with some vegetable seasoning and nut meal. For each grain, the number of different styles of cooking, is as varied as the number of grains!

PREPARATION OF VEGETABLES

Use an abundance of raw vegetables whenever possible. There are some starchy vegetables (rutabagas, potatoes, beets, etc.) whose nutrients may be better utilized by the body, when properly cooked. Therefore, all should learn the best way to cook vegetables, that they may show to their best advantage; by **appearance, flavor, and food value**. Raw, steamed or creamed vegetables can be very attractive and delicious. An easy way to cream some vegetables (rutabagas, greens, peas and potatoes, etc.), after cooking them lightly; is to add a little onion and garlic powders and dribble about 2 T sesame tahini (per qt. of veg.) over them and stir gently. Salt them lightly. Add a little fresh lemon juice for a mild cheese flavor, if you so desire.

Succulent vegetables (summer squash, etc.) should be cooked especially lightly and with only 1–3 T of water to start the steam. Overcooking makes some vegetables mushy, and partially destroys the coloring and flavor and nutritive value. Too much "peeking" lengthens the cooking time, by allowing the steam to escape.

Steaming is a good way to cook vegetables without excessive loss of nutrients. You may easily purchase a folding steamer rack for this purpose. Do not crowd vegetables in the steamer rack, and salt them just before serving, if at all. They may also be cooked nicely in a heavy saucepan with a tightly fitting lid, using only a **little** water, to form steam. The water left after cooking should be used in some way.

Bicarbonate of soda should **never** be used as a color preserver for greens, nor as a conditioner in cooking legumes and grains. It destroys part of the nutritive value of the food, and also leaves a harmful residue.

Whenever possible, vegetables should be served the same day they are gathered. If necessary to store vegetables for a period of time, do not put them in water, as this will dissolve minerals and vitamins (especially if they are cut up) and promote spoilage. Store them in a cold place. Frozen foods should be used immediately after being thawed and should not be refrozen, as a rule. Handle vegetables with care, as bumping, squeezing or bruising may release autolytic enzymes, which hasten spoilage.

SPROUTING SEEDS

ADVANTAGE OF SPROUTING—Seeds can be kept dry for many months or even years and are still suitable for sprouting (if properly stored). The sprouting process accomplishes biologically what grinding does through the use of physical means, and heating does through chemical changes. The chemical bonds for long term storage of nutrients are broken through the sprouting process, making them more easily available for use by the body. Additionally, there is the development of vitamins C, A, and B, and the development of chlorophyll. Sprouting is said to increase the content of vitamins B_1 and B_2, niacin, pantothenic acid, pyridoxine, biotin, and folic acid.

SEEDS TO BE SPROUTED—Just about any seed that will grow can be sprouted in a jar and used in cooking, or as a fresh food. A favorite is alfalfa, followed by radish and sunflower seeds (for salads). All the legumes (especially lentils, soybeans, and mung beans) are suitable for sprouts. Quick steaming of bean sprouts makes for a milder flavor. Lettuce, radishes, and similar plants that "go to seed," furnish good seeds for sprouting.

USES FOR SPROUTS—In winter, when greens are in short supply and are expensive in the market, sprouts can be prepared in the kitchen for use at a very inexpensive price. You can do gardening in your own kitchen. This kind of gardening requires no weed killing and no mulching! With judicious planning, sprouts may always be ready for use.

Sprouts may be used with a little salad dressing or mayonnaise, or combined with other items, as a tossed salad. Grated beets or carrot with alfalfa sprouts, make a fine salad. Bean sprouts used as a main dish are very good, in a loaf, in burgers, or simply sauteed with onion, a little soy sauce, etc. The cooking time for legumes is thus greatly reduced (to about 30 minutes; less for lentils), even for difficult-to-cook beans, such as garbanzos and soybeans.

METHOD—The simplest method for preparing sprouts is by using a half gallon jar with a jar ring and a wire screen or piece of clean nylon mesh fabric. Three tablespoons of whole seeds are placed in the half gallon jar with a generous quantity of water to soak overnight. The next morning, the seeds are rinsed well through the wire screen or nylon. The jar is turned upside down to drain for a few seconds and then left with a kitchen towel covering the jar to make a dark place. The seeds should be rinsed twice daily (more frequently in hot weather, to prevent spoilage). Gently distribute the seeds around the sides of the jar by turning and shaking. The wet seeds will adhere to the jar wall. Some think that sprouting is hastened by covering the jar with a towel, until the seeds sprout, and then uncovering. Sprouts are ready for use when ¼ to ½ inch long. Alfalfa seeds can be allowed to develop up to 1–2 inches long. After two days, place the jar in the sun to develop the chlorophyll. Rinse the sprouts in water to eliminate infertile seeds and hulls.

LEGUMES

Beans, peas, garbanzos, soybeans, lentils, and peanuts are all legumes. Legumes may be served in many delicious ways; alone, or in combination with a whole grain. Dry legumes should be rinsed, soaked (1) in cold water overnight or (2) brought to a **boil**, left to soak for an hour or more, with a tight lid on sauce pot and the heat turned off. Then cook them until they are **very tender**. Season beans with onion, or other seasoning and salt, or as you prefer. **Wait** to add salt or other seasoning **until** the beans are tender, or it will prolong the time of cooking. Let the beans simmer for a while with the seasonings, before serving. **Long, slow** cooking or **pressure cooking**, renders legumes the most digestible and tasty. When used with whole grain bread, dumplings, rice or pastas, they provide complete protein, good quality carbohydrates and fats, vitamins, minerals and fiber. See recipe section of this book for proportions for cooking legumes.

A small pressure cooker and canner pressure cooker (21 Qt. size is suggested) are a real asset for any home, in preparing legumes or canning vegetables (which cannot be canned safely by hot water bath canning method). The dry legumes may be soaked overnight in jars (1¼ cup dry beans per quart and cold water to fill jar), then pressured at 10–15 lbs. pressure for 1 hour, more for 2 qt. jars. (Lower pressure is needed at lower altitudes and higher pressure at higher altitudes.) They are then ready for easy use later. Or they may be cooked loose, in a deep pan placed inside a smaller pressure cooker, for 45 min. to 1 hr., depending on the variety of bean. Whether one uses the long-cooked method, or the pressure cooker, the main goal is to cook the beans so thoroughly that they start to fall apart, and even the skin is perfectly soft. Soft water helps them cook more quickly than hard water. Well cooked and seasoned beans, lentils or peas have a delicious flavor!

IF LEGUMES GIVE YOU "GAS" PROBLEMS

1. Make sure that you are on the **total health lifestyle** (including plenty of outdoor exercise, water and **simple** menus).

2. Be sure that the beans are **well cooked** (skin of bean as well as inside portion should not resist when pressed between fingers). Some find it helpful to soak beans, freeze them and then cook them until soft. **Sprouting legumes** before cooking them, greatly reduces their gas-forming potential. Try soaking them overnight, parboiling 15 minutes, discard water and add more, then finish cooking.

3. Try using a smaller helping and chewing them very well.

4. Some use a sprinkle of papaya enzyme (added by the individual, at the table).

5. Use the legumes that cause you little or no problem (lentils and pintos seem to be best for some people, for example).

THE USE OF FRUITS

The more fresh fruit used, the better (in most cases), as long as vegetables and whole grain products are not neglected. Use largely of the in season fruits. They are more economical and more nutritious than cold storage items. Whole fruits are more nutritious than fruit juices, as they contain the fiber and more vitamins, etc. But nothing, not even fruit juice, should be taken between meals. This health destroying practice upsets the circadian rhythms of the body and helps cause blood sugar imbalances. Plain, ripe, fresh fruit makes a delicious dessert for the re-educated appetite. There are also other simple desserts which may be made, such as fruit pies or cookies, sweetened with dates or other sweet fruit. Applesauce and other canned or frozen fruits may be served hot or cold over pancakes or cereal, as an alternative to milk or syrups.

NUTS AND SEEDS

Nuts and seeds are a very pleasant part of the diet. They are concentrated foods and should be used in small quantities. Frying nuts makes them more difficult to digest. Finely ground seeds and nuts greatly enhance the flavor of soups, vegetables, gravies, spread, breads, crackers, etc. The nutty flavor goes farther in this way, than when using whole or chopped nuts (in recipes). Nuts should be refrigerated or frozen after being shelled. Health food stores carry a variety of natural butters, ground from **lightly** toasted nuts or seeds, which may be used in place of margarine. Sesame tahini (made from hulled seeds) and peanut butter are often chosen as staples, for economy and flavor. Tahini is mild and may be used as a creamer, as well as a spread (Joyva is a good brand to look for).

MENU PLANNING IDEAS

GENERAL RULE—Eat a wide variety of unrefined foods: Fruits, vegetables, whole grain breads and cereals, legumes, nuts, and seeds. Prepare these in as simple and natural a manner as practical, eating only enough to satisfy hunger and to maintain ideal weight. You will automatically meet all nutritional needs for optimal health and performance (if you also incorporate the other 7 health laws, as given in the beginning of this book),

SIMPLICITY—This is one of the **great principles of life.** Every aspect of life should reflect this profound feature. The lifestyle, from possessions to the manners taught ones' children, may reveal this godlike quality. **Simplicity does not imply carelessness** or halfheartedness. Both of these characteristics reveal weakness of the fabric of the personality. **To make a simple lifestyle the pattern of the life, requires dedication**, as the tendency of modern life is always toward more complexity, more sophistication, more gloss and veneer.

WHY A MEAL PLANNER?—It saves time and mental exertion, wondering if the family is getting the proper nourishment. It eliminates wondering what was served yesterday, the day before, etc. It helps you figure the cost of meals, to use a variety of foods, and to prepare staple foods in a variety of ways. It aids you in making out your shopping list, and helps you be able to shop less often, by good planning. It helps you plan your garden; what and how much to plant. It also helps you know how much to can or freeze, of various items.

Plan your meals so that a **small variety of food satisfies all your taste needs**. Plan the main part of the meal of bland tasting foods, such as potatoes, pinto beans, or bread. Serve a salad with a tart dressing, a bit of honey, sweet potato, melons, or some other slightly sweet food with vegetable meals. This type of meal will satisfy, with a small variety of food. One tends to overeat, in trying to satisfy the appetite, if the meal consists of **all** bland tasting foods, for example.

Serve a small variety of foods at one meal, but have plenty of each dish. Every extra dish takes time and energy to prepare, and raises the cost of the meal. A large variety at a meal also tempts the family to overeat. It makes digestion more difficult, which in turn brings on a great number of diseases. Prepare **simple** dishes in order to save time and money. Everything that is added to a food makes it that much more expensive. Complicated dishes cost more, take more time and work to prepare, and often make the food harder to digest. But, be **sure** dishes are nicely seasoned and served with eye appeal.

Use more fresh fruit and vegetables. Prepare and serve foods as near their natural state as possible. This saves much labor and expense. Devitalized foods are expensive, as they rob the body of needed nutrients, and we pay for them again, when we finally break down and visit the doctor!

THE MOST IMPORTANT MEAL—Breakfast should be a well planned, attractively served meal, which contains about one half of the day's food requirements. Plenty of time should be allowed for eating. Breakfast is the most important meal of the day. The benefit to be derived from the food depends a great deal on how long the food remains in the mouth. Thorough chewing and an unhurried attitude are essential parts of this meal. No sense of haste should be allowed.

Carefully avoid using too much of concentrated foods and over-enriching foods with nuts, wheat germ, seeds, salt, or sugars. Rich foods are difficult for the body to handle. "Extra protein" is not needed. Eat a variety of unrefined fruits, nuts, and grains. It is better to use whole fruit, such as grapefruit and oranges, than the juices made from them. The pulp is valuable nutritionally. If you must buy canned fruit, you can get it without sugar in most markets. However, ripe, home canned or frozen fruit is the best.

Plan interesting and varied menus. Cook something with an irresistible aroma to stimulate morning appetites. Try the two meal plan, leaving off supper. Breakfast appetites will be hearty and digestive disorders will disappear. Get a good night's sleep on a **regular** basis. **Introduce changes gradually.** You will be well repaid.

LUNCH MAKING—Here is an opportunity to do something for someone you love! Plan for lunches when you shop or cook. Making lunches, day after day and year after year, could become a real chore, unless we fully realize how important the contents of each lunch are, for the overall nutrition of our families. You may follow the general menu planner in this section, and refer to the sandwich fillings in our recipe list. Avoid the morning rush by having the lunch mainly prepared the evening before.

The wide mouth **thermos bottles can be a great asset** to lunch making. Something nice and **cold** (fruit salad or sauce) or **hot** (fruit or vegetable soup; chowder or cooked cereal), as the weather may call for, is **very refreshing**. This also helps to cut down on the desire for many fancy sandwiches or desserts and the desire to drink with a meal. Add to this, good homemade crackers, corn bread, or tasty sandwiches and some fresh fruit **or** vegetable. Something piping hot **or** nice and cold from the thermos, really makes a lunch a success! Simple and delicious meals may thus be prepared for trips, avoiding expensive restaurant fees and poor nutrition.

BASIC RULES OF MENU PLANNING

1. Plan the menu ahead; about a week or so.

2. **Appetite satisfaction** depends on **variety** in: **color, texture, and taste experiences** (sweet, sour, savory and bland) **at every meal**. Following this rule, will ensure having a balanced diet, if only whole or unrefined foods are used.

3. **Good food: looks** good, **smells** good, **tastes** good, and has **high quality nutrients**. It is inexpensive, easy-to-prepare, harmless, and served on schedule (with at least 5 hours, between meals).

4. **Serve raw fruits or vegetables** at every meal.

5. **Limit liquid foods,** as this slows digestion (plenty of water between meals regulates thirst at mealtime).

6. **Serving and eating:** with **beauty, order, punctuality, cheerfulness, and surprises**.

7. **Combinations:** Avoid combining fruits and vegetables at the same meal. Use good whole grain products and fruits at one meal, and whole grains and vegetables at the next. Olives, avocado and nuts and seeds may be used with either fruit or vegetable meals. Some vegetable/fruits seem to go well with either, fruit or vegetable menus, such as: Tomatoes, melons or pineapple (actually a swollen plant stem). Experience will show each individual, which simple combinations agree with him/her best. No elaborate food combination charts are needed (it gives a person indigestion just to study some of the complicated charts!). Following are two simple definitions of fruits and vegetables.

> **Fruit**—The product of a blossom and contains the seed.
> **Vegetable**—Parts of a green plant (root, stem, leaves, blossom and green pod).

BASIC MENU OUTLINE

BREAKFAST

> **Fresh Fruit**—(use fruit in season, when possible)
> **Whole grain Cereal**—(cooked cereal, waffles, granola, etc.)
> **Milk or Fruit Sauce**, opt.—(soy, nut grain or banana milk or fruit sauce,
> to use over cereal)
> **Whole grain Bread**—(raised or unleavened bread, muffins, toast, etc.)
> **Spread or Side Dish**, opt.—(nut grain butter, fruit spread, olives, savory beans etc.)

DINNER (those with hypoglycemia feel better when using a vegetable breakfast)

Fresh Vegetable or Salad—(sliced tomatoes, simple salad, etc. Include dark greens or sprouts often.)
Main Dish—(a starchy vegetable—potatoes, winter squash, etc., legumes or legume/grain combination)
Cooked or Raw Vegetable—(greens, carrots, summer squash, broccoli, etc.)
Whole grain Bread—(bread, crackers, corn bread, biscuits, etc.)
Spread, Salad Dressing or Side Dish—(mayonnaise, nut butter, olives, etc.)

SUPPER (should be light, and taken several hours before bedtime, if taken at all)

Fruit— (fresh, canned, or frozen) Hot tomato soup and popcorn is nice on a cold evening. Cold watermelon makes a nice warm weather, light meal.
Whole grain Bread—(zwieback, popcorn, crackers, toast, unleavened bread, etc.)

***Always remember to include a variety in: ***

Colors
Textures
Taste Experiences

SAMPLE MENU PLANNER

	BREAKFAST	DINNER	DAILY MEMO
Sunday	Blueberries & Apples Granola Rice ~ Nut Milk Toast Nut Butter	Tomatoes & Parsley Garbanzos & Dumplings Bread Mayonnaise Lemon Pie	Granola Butter Cornbread Soak pinto beans
Monday	Oranges & Bananas Fluffy Cooked Rice Banana Milk Better Biscuits Fruit Butter	Sprouts & Tomatoes Pinto Beans Skillet Okra Cornbread & honey Mayonnaise	Make up waffle batter Nut Butter Defrost refrigerator Wash clothes
Tuesday	Grapes & Apples Waffles Hot fruit Sauce Toast Nut Butter	Tossed Salad Baked Potatoes Tomato Gravy, Greens Bread & Popcorn Salad Dressing	Nut Butter Make bread Wash windows
Wednesday	Pears & Apples Oatmeal Creamy Peach Sauce (blend canned peaches) Toast Nut Butter	Cole Slaw Spanish rice Bread & Nut Spread Cantaloupe	Soak Beans Corn Crackers Cook cornmeal mush Gravy + chill Town trip
Thursday	Grapefruit & Peaches Browned Cornmeal Mush Gravy or Canned fruit Toast Nut Butter	Sliced tomatoes Sunflower Mayonaise Mexican Bean Soup Sweet Potatoes Corn Crackers	Cornbread Nut milk Peanut Butter
Friday	Oranges & Bananas Raisins Cornbread Nutmilk Toast & Peanut butter	Carrot Salad Potato soup Green Beans Bread or Rolls Avocado or Spread	Crackers Split Pea Soup fruit Butter Almond butter Cook millet with raisins
Sabbath	Strawberries Millet with raisins Banana milk Toast Almond butter	fresh fruit Split pea soup Pioneer crackers fruit butter frozen fruit	Take fruit out in A.M.

Supper Suggestions

1. A light soup with crackers or popcorn
2. fresh or canned fruit with toast or popcorn

A light supper will not disturb your sleep like a heavy one.

ABBREVIATIONS

T	— Tablespoon	qt	— Quart
t	— Teaspoon	oz	— Ounce
c	— Cup	lb	— Pound
ww	— Whole Wheat	pkg	— Package
pt	— Pint	opt.	— Optional
HP	— Hydrogen Peroxide		

SPECIAL TERMS AND INGREDIENTS

Blanch—To place food in boiling water for a short period (such as tomatoes, peaches or almonds) to make peeling easy.

Blenderize—To liquify or grind in an electric blender.

Carob—A healthful chocolate substitute. Sold as a powder. It is best to make your own carob treats, as the commercial carob products are usually loaded with sugars, artificially hardened fats and dried whey.

Chicken Style Seasoning—*McKay's* Chicken Style Seasoning is made with or without white pepper or monosodium glutamate (MSG). This book also includes a recipe for chicken style seasoning, in case you can't obtain the above. Look for natural food sources under next section heading.

Coconut—The unsweetened, natural coconut is called for in our recipes.

Crisp Topping—A crumbly topping of flour, oats, vanilla over sliced fruit and baked until nicely browned.

Dextrinize—To lightly brown or toast, over medium heat in a dry skillet or in the oven. This will shorten the cooking time for grains, adding a more nutty flavor and a fluffier texture.

Dodger—Small cake of sweet potato, cornmeal or oatmeal, baked in a hot oven, until chewy inside and crisp outside.

Emes **gelatin**—a purely vegetarian product, which works like Jello, and comes in many flavors. Some of our recipes call for the plain or unflavored *Emes* gelatin. Most health food stores carry it or would be willing to. See natural food sources under next section heading.

Ener-G **Baking Powder**—We thought there was no safe baking powder until we discovered this one. It is simply citric acid and calcium carbonate (the form that doctors often give for calcium supplements). We recommend that it be used only occasionally, so there is no danger of taking in too much calcium. You could ask your health food store to carry it, so you won't have to pay the minimum p/h for just one item. At present it is sold only in 5½ oz. packages **or** bulk rate, in 20 lb. lots, from the producers. After trying it, several families might want to go in together on a 20 lb. amount as it is **much** cheaper per lb. that way. The address is: *Ener-G* Foods, Inc., 5960 1st Ave. S., P. O. Box 84487, Seattle, WA. 98124-5787. Phone: 1-800-331-5222.

Hydrogen Peroxide—My second choice for a quick leavening agent. Walmart's Crystal brand and some others have no additives, and leave no irritating residue. Since the fizz action may oxidize a few vitamins, it would be best to learn to use unleavened bread and **well baked** yeast breads most of the time. They are delicious when well prepared! For the **occasional** cake or cookies, there should be no problem. 3% Hydrogen Peroxide solution is what is called for in a few recipes in this book (for those who can't obtain the above baking powder, or do not wish to take in any extra calcium).

Instant Clear Gel (ICG)—A precooked cornstarch from a waxy variety of corn. It requires no cooking and remains creamy after thickening, so it is nice for a fresh berry topping (blenderize about ⅓ of the raw berries you plan to use, with a little ICG, vanilla, etc. and add this to the whole berries). A small amount of

ICG added to a seed or nut salad dressing (while blending) makes for a smoother texture, without extra richness (as with oil). Manufactured by Dutch Valley Food Distributors, Inc., Rt. 501 N., P.O. Box 465, Myerstown, PA 17067. Telephone 800/733-4191.

Legumes—Beans, peas, peanuts, garbanzos or lentils.

Lemon Juice—Used in place of vinegar (a stomach irritant).

Nut meal—Finely ground raw nuts or seeds. The easiest method for baking needs: grind the nuts with some of the dry flour called for in a recipe—especially helpful in making pie crust or crackers!

Nuts and Seeds—These are interchangeable in many recipes. Sunflower seeds, peanuts and coconut are most economical in many parts of the USA. Other nuts and seeds add a variety of rich flavors and nutrients to many recipes. Used sparingly, they are a real asset!

Orange Peel—Save nice orange peelings, cut up in squares and dry in a warm (not hot) place until crisp. Blenderize into a powder and store in a cool dry place in tight container. Used for a flavoring.

Parboil—A short boiling of food in water, in preparation for freezing, or for another purpose.

Rolled Oats—"Old Fashioned" refers to large flake rolled oats, and "Quick Oats" to the small flake preparation.

Sesame Seeds—Available hulled or unhulled. The hulled seeds are milder in flavor, but the unhulled variety are **much** higher in calcium content.

Soy Flour—Ask for the full fat or whole bean flour (**lightly** roasted), as the defatted or raw flour is not as tasty and/or nutritious.

Soy Milk Powder—A partially refined milk powder, made from soybeans. There are many such products on the market now and some are filled with sugar and oxidized fats. So read your labels and choose the simple preparations. We just use a little as a creamer in some recipes, rather than drinking it wholesale. We don't need to drink milk once we are weaned anyway! You may be as delighted as we were to discover **Soy Supreme** (reduced fiber). I had tried the **regular** Soy Supreme before and found it rather gritty and strong in flavor. The reduced fiber variety is mild and smooth in texture and is about half the price of regular soy milk powders! Some fiber is removed, but nothing else is added or subtracted. It is easy to flavor your own product as you wish. For a source see Natural Food Sources under next section heading.

Soy Sauce—We recommend only the unfermented variety. La Choy makes both a fermented and non-fermented soy sauce. The one labeled "Oriental Style" is fermented and the other is not. The salt in soy sauce will not be a drawback if you include it as part of the salt in a recipe.

Sweetening—Honey, date sugar, *Sucanat* (from unrefined cane juice) fruit juice concentrate etc. (all concentrated sugars, natural or partially refined) should be used sparingly. Manufactured by NutaCane, Inc., 5 Meadowbrook Parkway, Milford, NH 03055.

Starch—As used in our recipes, indicates cornstarch, arrowroot or other starch of your choice.

Tahini—A seed butter (on the liquid side) made from lightly toasted, **hulled** sesame seeds, not to be confused with sesame butter which is thicker, darker (usually burned) and made from the unhulled seeds. The former is mild and nice for adding a richer flavor to soups, potato salad, bean spread or even sweet treats. Joyva is the best brand we know of. Check Natural Food Sources in next section.

Zwieback—Thinly sliced bread or waffles (cut in strips) baked in a slow oven until thoroughly dried out and then **slightly** browned all the way through. Keeps well for trips and is easily digested.

EXPLANATIONS AND COOKING TIPS

Aluminum—Aluminum is presently under scrutiny as a cause of Alzheimer's disease (early senility). Though all evidence is not yet in, it is recommended that we avoid products containing aluminum: baking powders, artificial flavorings, many deodorants, cheap aluminum cookware which pits and discolors easily, and **especially** the use of soft drinks canned in aluminum (as the drinks have an acid content).

Baker's Yeast—When baking regularly it is more economical and ensures product freshness to buy yeast in vacuum-packed pkgs. by the lb. (store in refrigerator or freezer after opening). Of the regular action yeasts we have found Fleischmann's to be better than Red Star. But we prefer Instant SAF yeast which works more quickly, requires less per cup of dough and leaves less of a yeasty taste in the bread. It is sensitive to cool temperature and will just quit working if chilled too much.

Bread Flours—Hard winter or spring wheat is the best for making yeast raised breads, due to the higher gluten content. Of these, the hard **spring** wheat is the best, but hard winter will do. Soft wheat is best for biscuits, pie crust, crackers etc., as it is more starchy and will yield a more tender crisp (non-chewy) texture.

Brewer's Yeast—Also called Nutritional yeast flakes or powder, may be used sparingly as a seasoning. They add a cheese-like flavor to certain recipes. Both brewer's yeast and active yeast can raise the uric acid level in the blood, if used **freely**, thus making one more susceptible to gout. Of course all flesh meats are high in purines (especially organ meats and shell fish).

Cleaning Burned Pots—Try using the sharp edge of a canning lid or flat as a scraper. A minute timer might prevent such an accident.

Crying over Onions?—It's helpful to cut out all of the dark part of the root end of a onion, then leave it set aside for a minute or two (to drain). Running under cold water after cutting in half helps also.

Freshen up dry Rolls or Muffins—Put rolls in a dampened paper bag and place in microwave oven for 10 to 30 seconds or place on a vegetable steaming basket, and put in a kettle with a little water below basket for steam. Steam long enough to heat thoroughly.

Greasing or Oiling Pans—Vegetable shortening works nicely for greasing pans, as it spreads easily in a thin film. Another option is a solution of one part oil and one part liquid lecithin, (shake well in a small jar). It may be applied sparingly with a small cloth or tissue.

Mushrooms—We do not include recipes calling for mushrooms as studies show they contain aflatoxins (cancer promoting substances).

Natural Food Sources—Many good foods can be found in a regular grocery store: produce, some raw nuts, dried fruit, ww pasta, brown rice, rolled oats, dry beans, frozen fruits and vegetables and naturally sweet canned fruit, etc. Whole grain flour and cornmeal that we have noticed in the regular groceries, are not of the best quality however. A good variety and quality of whole grains, nuts and seeds are best found in a health food store, food co-op, by mail order, or from a local farmer. If you have a freezer or cooler space (or at least during the cooler months) you can save a lot by buying in bulk! Places to order these items are: Country Life Natural Foods, Oak Haven, PO Box 489, Pullman, MI 49450, Telephone: (616) 236-5011, Clear Eye Natural Foods, 302 Rt. 89 South, Savannah, NY 13146, Telephone: (800) 724-2233, Walnut Acres, Walnut Acres Rd., Penns Creek, PA 17862, Telephone: (800) 433-3998, and Weimar Institute Product Orders, PO Box 486, Weimar CA 95736, Telephone: (916) 637-4111.

Nonstick Bakeware—T-Fal or Silverstone are the best nonstick bakeware we know of to date. If treated with care they last well. If these products are not feasible for you, you may choose a regular baking pan or skillet and prepare the surface with a film of the above oil-lecithin preparation or other. Heavy metal or glass pans help brown food evenly without burning. A cast iron skillet (seasoned) works best for pancakes.

Oat Flour—This may be easily made by blenderizing rolled oats in about 1½ c. portions in your blender. Oats have a rich flavor so are tasty used as a thickening agent in soups, stews, or even fruit soup. Barley flour is also an excellent thickener.

36

Prevent Dough from Sticking to Hands—Moisten hands and counter with warm water just before forming a lump of bread dough into a loaf. This method leaves little mess on the work surface and does not cause separations in the loaf, as do oil or flour.

Proportions for Cooking Grains and Legumes—When using them in our recipes, it is best to use our recommended proportions of water etc., for best recipe results.

Remove Scorch Flavor—From beans, soup, etc. Do not stir or scrape the bottom of pan when you sense a problem. Wipe the outside bottom of the kettle with a very wet, cold cloth or small towel for a few seconds. Then dump the contents quickly into another container, without scraping stuck portion. Cold water draws the scorch flavor to the bottom of the kettle.

Rolling Pin—The best kind I know of for some jobs is an 8 or 9 inch length of unpainted, broom handle size dowel stick. Sand it thoroughly to remove any rough spots or edges. Oil generously with any vegetable edible oil to seal wood pores, and let oil soak in for a day, then wipe dry. Rolling pin should be washed and dried after each use. One can apply direct pressure as this little tool rolls under both hands—in rolling out flour tortillas, pie crust, or crackers.

Seasoning Cast Iron Pans—Heat pan thoroughly, rub evenly with Crisco or other vegetable oil, then wipe off with a dry tissue or cloth. One or two such coatings is sufficient for a batch of pancakes, if baking temperature is not so high that they burn easily.

Soybeans—For a milder flavor we recommend the yellow-tan edible soybeans (not the black-eye variety). Some of our recipes call for soaked soybeans. They should be soaked overnight in plenty of cold water, they will double in bulk and may be kept in the refrigerator for several days if need be. They may be used as a leavening in some recipes by blending them in cold water until very creamy, then folding the flours into this light mixture. We include a recipe for a delicious cheese cake in our dessert section which uses soaked soybeans.

Upper Case—(All capital letters.) Ingredients thus marked in our recipes, are those for which there is a recipe included in the book.

Waffles—A good bread substitute! For those with a wheat or all gluten grains intolerance, waffles make a wonderful bread. We make up a big batch of them and freeze most of them for later use. Twice-baked waffle sticks (zwieback) are great for taking on trips. You might like to try **"Favorite 3-Grain Waffles"** for a starter if you have not made them before. A good nonstick waffle iron will take only 1 or 2 light sprays of Pam or the equivalent, for a whole batch of waffles.

Raised Breads

RAISED BREADS

It is a sacred **duty for every girl and woman to learn** to make good, light bread from **unrefined** flour. Mothers should take their daughters into the kitchen with them, when very young, and teach them the art of cooking. She should instruct them patiently, lovingly, and make the work as agreeable as she can, by her cheerful countenance and encouraging words. If a love for cooking and other necessary domestic duties is once implanted, it will never be lost! It will also prove a real safeguard from idle moments during the restless teens, and will help prepare a young woman for a happy home of her own. Today much **worthless information** is passed on to youth, in the name of "education", while the earnest **duties of life are passed over**, with hardly a mention. Good cooking is one of the most essential branches of education, especially for young women.

The staff of life is bread, our most important food. Breads are of two types: (1) raised or light breads and (2) unleavened breads. We will present raised breads, leavened with yeast or *Ener-G* baking powder (calcium and citric acid), as baking soda and regular baking powders either leave irritating residues in the food or destroy some of the vitamins. The volatile substances left in yeast breads, from the growth process of the yeast, evaporate within 1–3 days. The conditioning of the crumb also proceeds during this time, making the bread more digestible and easier to cut.

The whole grains contain a large number of vitamins, and minerals, as well as carbohydrates, protein, fats, and dietary fiber. Use only the freshest and best quality flours possible. It is well to keep all flours refrigerated or frozen during storage. The high gluten content of hard wheat makes it best for bread making. Breads made from mixtures of two or three grains should be used alternately with single grain breads for best nutrition. You need not mix a **large** number of grains in one loaf.

TIPS FOR SUCCESS IN BREAD MAKING—Never start a batch of bread until you have read the recipe all the way through, know that you have the proper ingredients or suitable substitutes, and understand the mixing method.

If you are just learning to bake, try a simple basic recipe first, such as **"Basic Whole Wheat Bread"**. For regular loaf bread, we have found the **hard spring wheat** to be the best and **hard winter wheat** comes in second. One has to get the best he can obtain in his area. Soft wheat has a lower gluten content and is nice for making muffins, pie crust or biscuits.

An off flavor develops in bread that is allowed to get too warm. Too cool a temperature prolongs the rising. Yeast grows best at a temperature of about 85° F. Cover the bowl of dough to prevent heat from escaping, or the dough from drying out (another bowl upside down or a large piece of plastic will do the job).

Salt retards the action of yeast, so should not be added until after some flour has been added to the yeast mixture.

Develop the gluten in bread dough, by beating with a spoon, a potato masher, or electric hand mixer, then kneading and letting the dough rise several times. Be careful not to allow the dough to over-rise by letting it rise too long before kneading it down each time. This makes the bread have a course, crumbly grain. Gluten toughens when it is beaten, enabling it to hold air bubbles better.

Always preheat the oven **before** the bread is ready to go in. It is best to turn it on a little before you start molding the loaves, as this warms the kitchen and helps the bread rise quickly. Ten minutes preheating is minimal time for most ovens. Gas heated ovens may take longer than electric ones. It would be well to check your oven thermostat accuracy, with an oven thermometer, if you have any doubts about it.

When the dough is ready to be formed into loaves, divide it in equal parts, **press out** the bubbles, but do not knead vigorously, as when developing the gluten. To prevent sticking, moisten your hands and the kneading surface with a little warm water. Work quickly with the dough to prevent chilling it. Roll the dough into a thick roll with the "seam" underneath. Place it in a nonstick or lightly greased pan. After

41

forming the loaves, cover them with a towel and allow them to rise in a warm place for about 10–15 minutes (depends on the temperature, and how much yeast was used in the recipes).

Only practice will teach you just when the loaves are ready for the oven. They should be nearly doubled in bulk. If in doubt, it is **better to let it be a little on the "green" side, than over-raised**. The loaves should be thoroughly baked. No taint of sourness should be present in the bread when the loaf is cut.

Let the bread cool thoroughly before storing it in plastic bags, or the crust will become damp and will mold more easily. Brushing with oil is not necessary. Obtain a good sharp bread knife and learn to cut with a quick sawing motion, to prevent tearing the loaf. Nice, even slices help prevent "burning the toast".

In making whole wheat bread, the dough should be about as sticky as can be handled, when you **first** make up the dough. Yet if the dough is too wet, it will not have a good grain and will have a harder crust. This will come with practice. Whole-wheat bread dough does not rise as high as the white variety, as it carries a heavy freight of vitamins, minerals, and fiber which the refined dough does not. Making bread is not difficult, but does take care and thought and practice. Your efforts will be well repaid in better health.

BASIC WHOLE WHEAT BREAD

Yield: 3 medium or 4 small loaves

4 c very warm water	1 c raw seeds OR nuts
2 T baker's yeast	1 T salt
2 T sweetening	7½–8 c hard ww flour (hard spring wheat best)
1 c rolled oats	

Blenderize the nuts, oats, yeast and sweetening with enough of the warm water to blend them **smooth**. A six qt. kettle with lid works well for a mixing bowl. Stir in the remaining warm water, about 3½ c slightly warm flour and salt. Whip this batter for 2 full min. with an electric hand mixer **or** use a regular potato masher for at least 5 min. (depends how vigorously you work). You will see gluten strands forming. Next stir in the rest of the flour and finish mixing by hand. The dough should be a little sticky to start with, as it will firm up while rising. Flours vary a little, so you will learn by practice, just what consistency to look for., Cover and leave dough in a warmish spot to rise. If it is too warm, dough will have a sour flavor; if too cool, it won't rise well! Let it rise for about 20 min. or to double in size. Moisten hands in warm water and punch dough down thoroughly. Cover and let rise 1–2 more times, as this will help develop the gluten without so much kneading. Set your timer, as over-rising also gives an off flavor. When you are ready to form the dough into loaves, divide it into 3–4 equal parts. Moisten your hands and the counter top with warm water, to prevent sticking. If you work quickly with the dough, the water is more effective than flour or oil, in preventing sticking, (without causing separations through the loaf). Press, do not knead, the air bubbles out of each lump of dough, roll it up into a thick "log", and place it in a greased bread pan. Work quickly, so the loaves will be ready for the oven at nearly the same time. Cover the loaves with a dry towel, and allow them to rise in a warm place for 10–15 minutes. The loaves should rise until they have **nearly** doubled their size. Remember that they will rise a little more in the oven before the heat stops the action of the yeast. If the loaves turn out a little sunken or flat on top, they raised too much before they were put in the oven. If there are big cracks along the sides, they didn't rise quite long enough, or the dough was too dry.

Bake the bread at 375° F. for 20 minutes, then reduce the heat to 350° F. and bake for about 20 minutes longer. Do not open the oven unnecessarily, especially during the first 20 minutes, or the bread may fall. Small loaves take less time to bake than medium ones. (The above time and temperatures are for medium loaves.) Cool the bread on a rack or towel. When cool, put it in plastic bags and store in the refrigerator or freezer.

Thoroughly baked bread has a nutty flavor and is more healthful, as the yeast is killed. So we planned these loaves on the small side on purpose. Once you get used to making good whole grain breads, you won't be satisfied to be without it! Be sure to read the tips for good bread-making on the previous pages, if this is a new art for you.

BASIC MUFFINS

Yield: 1 dozen muffins

2 c very warm water OR fruit juice	3 c ww flour (hard)
1 T sweetening	½ c rolled oats
1 T yeast	½ c nuts OR ¼ c tahini
1 c chopped dried fruit OR dried fruit and nuts	1 t salt

Blenderize half of the flour, the nuts and oats until finely ground. Dissolve the sweetening in the water, then sprinkle in the yeast. Leave alone until the yeast pops up again. Have the four items at the right in a bowl, ready to stir into the yeast mixture as soon as the yeast pops up. You may want to add dried fruit and/or nuts, as suggested in the recipe, or you may add 2 ripe, cubed bananas and ½ c chopped pecans, walnuts or other nuts or seeds. Fill the muffin cups ⅔ full and let them rise for 8–10 minutes in a warm place. Have the oven preheated at 375° F. Bake for about 25–30 minutes at this temperature.

EASY BATTER BREAD

Yield: 3–4 loaves (good as raisin bread)

5 c very warm water	1 c rolled oats (OR rye flour)
2 T sweetening	1 c cornmeal
2 T yeast	7½ c hard ww flour (more or less)
1½ c raisins OR chopped dates, opt.	2½ t salt

Dissolve the sweetening in the water and sprinkle in the yeast. Leave it alone until the yeast pops to the surface. Then stir in all the other ingredients vigorously. Let the batter rise in a warm place for 20 minutes. Mix it well again with a spoon or by hand. Place the dough in 3 medium or 4 smaller bread pans (filled about ½ full). Smooth the top with a moistened rubber spatula. Let them rise for only 6–8 minutes in a warm place. It will rise more in the oven. Bake at 400° F. for 20 minutes, then reduce the heat to 350° F. and bake for 25–30 minutes longer. Cool on a rack.

CORN BREAD

Yield: one 8" X 10" pan

2 c very warm water	1¾ c ww flour (hard wheat)
1–2 T sweetening	1 t salt
1 T yeast	¼ c Nuts OR seeds (grind fine with some of the cornmeal)
2 c cornmeal	

Dissolve the sweetening in the warm water and sprinkle the yeast into the water. Leave it alone until the yeast pops up. Then stir in the other ingredients and beat with a wire beater or spoon. Let the batter rise in a warm place for 20–30 minutes. Whip the batter again with the beater or spoon. Turn it into muffin cups or a square or round baking pan and fill them/it about half full. Smooth over the top with a spoon or rubber spatula. Let rise in a warm place for 5–8 minutes. Bake at 375° F. for 40–45 minutes.

SIMPLE FRUIT CAKE VARIATION: Mix the following into the above **"CORN BREAD"** recipe, and turn into a Bundt or tube cake pan: ½ c chopped nuts, 1½ c chopped dates, ½ c ww flour, 1½ c drained, chunk pineapple (use the juice as part or all of the water for the recipe), grated rind from 2 oranges. Bake a little longer than directed for plain corn bread. It may be served plain or with **"LEMON SAUCE"**.

ZWIEBACK
(twice-baked bread)

Dry foods, that require thorough mastication, are more easily digested than soft or liquid foods. Zwieback, or twice-baked bread, is one of the most easily digested and palatable of foods. Let ordinary raised bread be cut in thin slices and dried in a warm oven (200° F.) until the last trace of moisture disappears. Then brown it **lightly** all the way through, at a slightly higher temperature. When stored in an airtight container, or plastic bag, this bread will keep well for long trips or for future use in the home.

RYE BREAD

Yield: 2–3 loaves

4 c very warm water	3 T ground OR whole caraway seed
2 T sweetening	5 c rye flour
2 T yeast	5 c ww flour (hard wheat)
⅓ c Blackstrap molasses	1 c rolled oats
1 T salt	1 c gluten flour or ww flour

Dissolve the 2 T sweetening in the warm water, then sprinkle the yeast in, and leave it alone until the yeast pops up. Next, add 3 c of the ww flour, the oats, and gluten flour. Stir thoroughly, cover and let it rise for 20 minutes in a warm place, to develop gluten strands. Then stir in the rye flour, and seasonings. Knead by hand, using enough more ww flour to make a soft dough. It will be sticky, but will firm up some as it rises again. Cover and let dough rise double in size (about ½ hour), then moisten hands and punch dough down. Repeat this a time or two. Form loaves into the shape and size you prefer (round, long, oval). Cover and allow to rise for 8–10 minutes in a warm place. Bake at 400° F. for 20 minutes. Reduce the heat to 350° F. and bake for 30–40 minutes longer, or until well baked. Cool on a rack.

DROP BISCUITS

Yield: serves 3–4

1 c soft ww flour	1⅛ c warm water (OR ⅞ c cold water if
1 c quick oats	using HP*)
2–3 T tahini	2 t sweetening
½ t salt	1½ T *Ener-G* baking powder* (OR ¼ c HP*)

Thoroughly cream together the items in the left column (by spoon, and by hand). Stir in the water and sweetening. Oven should be hot before adding the raising agent. Stir this in evenly with a wire whisk, then spoon batter onto nonstick cookie sheet quickly. Bake at 400° F. for about 30 min. Best served hot and fresh, but may be reheated in toaster.

* See Hydrogen Peroxide or Ener-G Baking powder information under "Special Terms and Ingredients"

OAT BISCUITS

Yield: 1 cookie sheet

2½ c very warm water	1½ t salt
2 T sweetening	4½ c hard ww flour
1½ T yeast	3 c oat flour (make in blender from rolled
½ c nuts (blend finely with oats)	oats)

Dissolve the sweetening in the warm water, then sprinkle in the yeast and leave it alone until the yeast pops up. Add all the other ingredients at once and stir together thoroughly. Moisten your hands in warm water, and quickly form the dough into round or oblong biscuits, about 1 inch thick. Place them on an oiled cookie sheet, cover and let them rise in a warm place for about 20 minutes. Bake at 400° F. for 15 minutes, then reduce the heat to 350° F. and bake for 20–25 minutes longer. A delicious, hearty bread!

QUICK CORN BREAD

Yield: 10 inch pan

1 c hard ww flour
2 c cornmeal
⅓ c nuts (OR 2½ T tahini)
1½ t salt

2¼ c very warm water (OR 1¾ c cold water with HP*)
1 T sweetening
2½ T *Ener-G* baking powder* (OR ⅓ c HP*)

Blenderize the flour with the nuts until nuts are finely ground (**or** cream the tahini into all the dry ingredients until well mixed). Have the oven preheated before mixing the baking powder into the batter. Mix the ingredients in the order given, after blending the nuts and flour. After mixing in the baking powder thoroughly, place the batter in a greased pan. Bake at 375° F. for 35 minutes or until well done. Best hot and fresh.

See Hydrogen Peroxide or Ener-G Baking Powder information under **"Special Terms and Ingredients"*

Unleavened Breads

UNLEAVENED BREADS

The free use of quick or unleavened breads, has many advantages. These breads are simple and often quick to make. The thorough baking of such breads as crackers, contributes to their digestibility and flavor. This is because the starches are dextrinized by the action of heat and water. They also require thorough mastication, which aids digestion in several ways. Whole grain products require longer baking than the refined flour products, but they are essential for good health.

SKILLET CORN BREAD
(rich natural corn flavor)

1½ c cornmeal
¼ c raw sunflower seeds
¾ t salt

1½ c boiling water
½ c cold water (last, to smooth it out)

Blenderize the seeds with the meal until they are finely ground. Add the salt to the meal and ground seeds in a bowl. Pour on the boiling water all at once and stir well with a wire whisk. Then whip in the cold water last. Place at once into a hot oil-sprayed skillet. Bake with lid on over a medium–low heat for 12–15 minutes on **each** side. Best freshly baked, but cooled a little.

CHAPATTIS
(flour tortillas)

Serves 2 to 4

2 c ww flour (hard wheat)
½ t salt

¾ c warm water (scant)

Place the flour and salt in a bowl and slowly stir in the warm water to make a soft dough. Knead until it is elastic and not sticky. Form into balls the size of golf balls. Dip the balls in flour, one at a time, and roll out to a 7 inch round (about ⅛ inch thick). Bake on a dry, medium-hot griddle or skillet (cast iron is best). When the upper side turns color, turn over for a few seconds, then return to the first side and press with a cloth, using a rotating motion. Watch it puff like a football! Use as you would a tortilla. It takes practice to make a chapatti round, but they taste good, regardless of the shape!

BANANA LOGS

Yield: 1 dozen sticks

1 c mashed, ripe banana OR persimmon
1 c rolled oats (OR ¾ c cornmeal)
2 c ww flour (hard wheat)
½ c coconut (grind with a cup of the
         wheat flour)

½ c soy flour OR other flour
½ t salt
1 t vanilla OR 1½ t grated orange rind

Put all the ingredients together in a bowl and mix thoroughly. Form into 4–6 inch long sticks, about the size of a man's thumb. Bake on a cookie sheet, at 350° F. for 35–40 minutes. Delicious hot or cold.

SESAME CRACKERS

Yield: 1 cookie sheet

¾ c very warm water
1 t sweetening
2 t active yeast

2–2½ c soft ww flour (slightly warmed)
⅓–½ c sesame seeds
¾ t salt

Blenderize the water, yeast, sweetening and sesame seeds for about 30 seconds or more. Pour it into a bowl and stir in 2 c of ww flour and the salt. Knead by hand with a little more flour to make a soft dough. Roll out thinly on an oiled or nonstick cookie sheet. Work quickly to prevent chilling the dough. Dust the rolling pin with flour to prevent the dough from sticking to it. A few sesame seeds may be sprinkled on top and pressed in with a rolling pin. Score, prick with a fork, cover with a towel and allow to rise in a warm place for 10–15 minutes. Bake at 350° F. for 15 minutes, then at 300° until they are crisp. Check the crackers often and turn them over when they are nearly done, to hasten the baking and drying. They should be completely dried out. When cool, store in an airtight container.

POPPING CORN WITHOUT OIL

The new hot air poppers are excellent for this purpose. One can learn to relish **freshly popped** corn with just a light sprinkle of fine popcorn salt. For a seasoned popcorn salt, you may mix onion, garlic, celery and paprika powders and a **little** nutritional yeast. Grind these as finely as possible in your blender and then add some of the fine popcorn salt to the mixture. If your grocery doesn't carry plain popcorn salt, you may find it in the shopping mall in a popcorn shop.

RICE CRACKERS
(bake on nonstick pans only)

Yield: 2 cookie sheets

1½ c cold water
½ c pecans OR other nuts (1/3 c will do)
½ t salt

2 c cooked rice
2 c quick oats

Blenderize the water, nuts and salt first, then add the cooked rice while this is blending, and blenderize thoroughly. Pour in a bowl and stir in the quick oats. Place half of the batter on each of two nonstick cookie sheets and smooth out as evenly as possible. Bake at 350° F. for 30 minutes, then score with a table knife. Turn the heat down to 300° F. and bake the crackers some more until they are crisp and dry. If you turn them when partially dry, they will dry faster. They should be lightly browned, but guard against burning. Pecans make them darker than other nuts do. They are delicious, crisp and easy-to-make.

SOY-CORN GEMS

Yield: 1 dozen muffins

2 c soaked, drained soybeans
(1 c dry beans or less)
1¾ c yellow cornmeal

1 T sweetening (opt.)
2 c very cold water
1 t salt

Blenderize all but the cornmeal, until very creamy and light (about a full minute). Pour into a bowl and stir in the cornmeal. Spoon the batter into well greased or nonstick muffin tins **or** cast iron gem pans. Preheated cast iron pans make a lighter product. Bake at 375° F. for 30–40 minutes—until golden brown, Best fresh.

OAT DODGERS

Yield: 1 cookie sheet

3 c cold water
3 c rolled oats
1 t salt, scant

⅓ c nuts (grind fine with the ww flour)
½ c ww flour, rounded

Mix these items together the night before (or at least 5 hours before), and place it in the refrigerator. Whip a few times with a spoon, then place by spoonfuls on a greased cookie sheet, and flatten a little with a spoon., Bake at 400° F. until they start browning slightly around the edges (about 45 minutes). Serve hot.

UNLEAVENED WHEAT BISCUITS
(chewy & delicious)

5–6 c ww flour (the amount varies with
    the type of flour and liquid used)
1–2 T sweetening

2 c soy OR other milk
2 t salt

Place flour and salt in a mixing bowl. Add the sweetening, then stir as you pour in the liquid, until it makes a firm dough. Knead the dough until it is quite elastic, using a little flour if needed. Roll out ½ inch thick and cut with a biscuit cutter. Bake at 400° F. for 40 minutes, or until lightly browned. Do not dry them out as they would be too hard.

CRISPY CORN CRACKERS
(only on nonstick cookie sheet)

Yield: 1 cookie sheet

2 t sweetening (opt.)
2½ c cornmeal
½ t salt

1 c warm water
½ c raw sunflower seeds OR raw nuts

Blenderize sunflower seeds and hot water until creamy (1 minute). Place this in a bowl and mix well with the salt, cornmeal and sweetening. Roll out evenly (pat by hand at first) on one nonstick cookie sheet with sides, using a water moistened rolling pin. Score as desired. Bake at 350° F. for 40 minutes or until crisp and slightly browned (not dark). Turn the crackers over after baking for 30 minutes, for quicker drying.

WHEAT THINS
(on the rich side)

Yield: 1 cookie sheet (thin)

1 c ww flour (soft)
⅓ t salt

½ c coconut OR pecan meal
5 T water (or less)

Blenderize ww flour and coconut until very fine. Combine all ingredients in a bowl and mix only enough to combine. Roll out thinly enough to cover one regular cookie sheet. Dust the rolling pin with flour to prevent sticking. Score and prick. Bake at 350° F. for 10 minutes, then reduce heat to 300° and bake for 10–15 minutes longer or until crisp. Turn the crackers over for the last few minutes, to help them dry out better. Watch carefully near the end of the baking time!

PIONEER CRACKERS
(healthful granola bar type)

Yield: 1 cookie sheet

5 c quick oats
½ c ww flour (hard)
1 c any raw nuts
1¼ t salt
1¼ c mashed banana OR any other thick,

sweet, mashed fruit (apple sauce, persimmons, etc.)
2 T honey (opt.)
2 t vanilla
1 t orange rind OR ½ t orange extract (opt.)

Blenderize the ww flour with nuts until very finely ground. Combine the dry ingredients, then prepare the mashed banana and add this and the other flavorings at once to the flour mixture. Mix quickly and thoroughly by hand, only enough to mix well. Press out evenly into one cookie sheet with sides, about ⅓ inch thick. Use a rolling pin to even out. Score as you wish, with a knife. Bake at 375° F. for 35 minutes, then turn crackers over, reduce heat to 350° F. and bake for 15 minutes longer, or until lightly browned (it depends on how hard or dry you like them). If baked until all moisture is gone, they will be too hard.

WHEAT-OAT CRACKERS

Yield: 1 cookie sheet

¾ c ww flour (soft)
¾ c quick oats
½ t salt

⅓ c coconut OR other nuts
¼ c cold water (approx)

Blenderize ww flour and nuts until fine. Mix the dry ingredients in a bowl. Add the water all at once and mix well. Roll the dough out thinly and evenly to cover one regular cookie sheet. Dust the rolling pin with flour to prevent it from sticking to the dough. Score as you wish. Bake at 400° F. for 15 minutes, then at 250° F. until **well** dried out and **lightly** browned. Best fresh, but good later if stored in airtight container or plastic bag.

Breakfast Cereals

BREAKFAST CEREALS

BASIC GRANOLA

Yield: 1 cookie sheet or 1 qt. cereal

4 c quick oats
¼ c ww flour
½ c nuts (any kind)
¾ t salt (or less)

1 t grated orange rind (opt.)
1 t vanilla extract
1 c sweet fruit juice OR ¾ c water +
    1 T honey

Blenderize the nuts with ww flour and 1 cup of the oats to a fine flour. Mix the dry ingredients well, then add the liquids and mix thoroughly, but do not press together. Sprinkle on one cookie sheet. Bake at 350° F. for 20 minutes, then 300° F. until the cereal is crisp, but only **slightly** browned. After it dries out, it will burn very easily if baked too long.

MILLET-RAISIN BAKE

Serves 4 to 6

6 c hot water
2 c soaked, parboiled and
    drained soybeans
1¼ t salt
2 t vanilla extract

1 T sweetening (opt.)
1½ c raisins
1¼ c uncooked millet OR 1⅓ c rice
⅔ c chopped nuts (opt.)

Blenderize the soybeans in 2 c of the hot water until very creamy. Combine this and the other ingredients in a nonstick or heavy weight saucepan. Bring to a boil, cover and turn the heat down low and simmer for 45 minutes, or more. Place in a casserole dish. Bake in a hot oven until the top browns lightly.

FRENCH TOAST DIP

Yield: 1½ c dip

1 c cold water
⅓ c cashew nuts OR other nuts
⅓ c rolled oats

¼ t salt OR to taste
1 T ww flour OR other flour
1 T honey (opt.)

Blenderize **half** of the water with the other ingredients, until it is very creamy. Add the rest of the water, and pour the batter into a soup bowl. Dip the bread slices quickly through the batter (both sides). Place at once on a hot seasoned cast iron or nonstick griddle, or bake on a cookie sheet in a 400° F. oven, for 20 minutes or until lightly browned.

OVEN PANCAKES

Yield: 10 small cakes

1½ c cold water
1 ¼ c soaked, drained soybeans
2 T ww flour

½ t salt
1 T sweetening
1½ c quick oats

Blend all but the oats until very creamy. Stir the oats in by hand. Place by ⅓ cupfuls on a nonstick (heavy pan best to prevent burning) cookie sheet. Smooth with the back of a spoon to ½ in. thick. Bake at 375° F. for about 35 min., until lightly browned.

BUCKWHEAT CAKES

Yield: Ten ¼ cup size cakes

1½ c quick oats	1 T sweetening
½ c buckwheat flour OR barley flour	½ t vanilla OR maple extract
½ c ww flour	½ t salt
¼ c nut meal (pecan is best)	2¼ c cold water

You can make nut meal by blending nuts with the flour in a blender. Dextrinize the oats in a dry skillet over a medium heat. Stir often until it smells nutty and turns **slightly** darker in color. If it turns brown, it will be burned. The dextrinizing should take only 8–10 minutes or less. Let the oats cool, then stir in the water and other ingredients. Let the mix set aside for a few minutes. Bake by ¼ c portions on a medium-hot seasoned cast iron griddle or skillet. When you see little holes forming all over the pancakes, you'll know it's time to turn them over the first time. Loosen the edges with care and they should turn nicely. Serve hot with the topping of your choice.

WHOLE GRAIN CREPES
(may be used as tortillas or thin pancakes also)

Yield: approximately 8 crepes

2 c water	½ c cornmeal
½ t salt	½ c ww flour
1½ c rolled oats	

Blenderize all ingredients together until creamy. Let stand for ½ hour. Then bake on a hot, seasoned cast iron griddle or skillet. If the griddle is kept clean between crepes, you won't need to re-oil it (provided the temperature is right). When the batter turns color a little, loosen the edges of the crepe with a turner, and it will turn nicely. About ¼ c of batter, when spread thinly, makes a nice sized crepe.

FRUIT CRISP TOPPING
(nice main dish for a fruit meal)

Yield: Tops one 6" X 12" casserole

1½ c quick oats	¼ c fruit juice concentrate of ¼ c fruit juice
¼ c ww flour	plus 1 T honey
1 t vanilla extract	⅓ c coconut meal OR other nut meal
⅓ t salt	

Combine dry ingredients in a bowl. Mix liquid with the flavorings and sprinkle this over the dry items. Mix well. Fill a 6" by 12" casserole dish nearly full of sliced, raw apples, peaches, etc. Or you may use canned fruit, thickened with oat flour (¼ c oat flour to 1 qt fruit). Crumble the above mixture over the fruit evenly and press down gently. Bake at 350° F. until the fruit and topping are well baked and the topping is nicely browned (about 45 minutes). Good plain or with a creamy nut milk. Choose one kind of fruit for one dish.

WAFFLE OR PANCAKE TOPPING IDEAS

You may like to use different naturally sweet canned fruit sauces with a little spread of some kind of nut butter. Simply blend the canned fruit until it is creamy, in the blender. You may also want to try our **"LEMON SAUCE"** or **"BANANA CAROB SAUCE"**, or a simple fruit jelly or jam. (See the recipes for these.) Mashed banana, whipped with a little peanut butter and vanilla, is also delicious. Slightly thickened sweet fruit juice (apple, grape, pineapple or orange, etc.), makes a delicious and healthful fruit syrup for waffles or pancakes.

FAVORITE 3-GRAIN WAFFLES
(easy and dependable)

Yield: 10 large waffles

6 c rolled oats	1 c raw sunflower seeds OR nuts
1½ c ww flour	1 T salt
2 c cornmeal	10 c cold water

Mix all the dry ingredients in a large bowl. Add the water all at once and stir with a wire whisk. Soak for a couple of hours or better, overnight. Mix again and then blenderize until creamy (never filling blender more than half full at one time). Pour directly into a hot nonstick waffle iron. Will not stick if iron is hot and you don't bring batter quite to edge. Bake on "dark" for about 10 minutes. These are good frozen and reheated in toaster. Just cut in quarters and freeze in a tight plastic bag.

GLUTEN-FREE WAFFLES

Yield: 10–12 medium waffles

3 c raw brown rice (whole)	3 c cooked, cooled millet (pack)
3½ c cornmeal	(see directions for cooking whole grains)
1 c raw sunflower seeds	1 T salt
9 c cold water	

Combine the ingredients in the left column and soak overnight. Cook millet the night before, or use leftover millet cereal (it should be plain, without dried fruit, etc.). Break up the millet if lumpy, add the salt and stir all ingredients together. Blenderize this mixture by half blenderfuls, trying to take up equal amounts of water and solids, as you go. Blend batter until creamy, and blend all of it and mix together again to assure even mixture. Use a light oil spray even with a nonstick iron, for the first and then every 3rd waffle. Bake on "dark" setting for 7–8 minutes. Freeze extra waffle sections in tight plastic bag, for reheating later in toaster. Makes an excellent bread alternative for those with celiac disease, or simply wheat intolerance.

COOKING DIRECTIONS FOR WHOLE GRAIN CEREALS

For 1 Cup of Dry Grain	Water	Cooking Time	Salt
Barley or Rye Flakes	3½ c	1–1½ hours	½ t per c
Millet	3¼ c	45–60 minutes	of dry grain
Brown Rice	3 c	1½ hours	
Rolled Oats ("Old Fashioned")	1½ c	30–45 minutes	
Bulgur Wheat	3 c	45 minutes	
Corn Grits or Cracked Wheat	3½ c	1½ hours	
Cornmeal (for mush)	3 c	1 hour	

GENERAL DIRECTIONS—Bring the required amount of water to a boil, then add the grain and salt. Cover and turn the heat down to low, so it will just boil gently and not boil over. Start counting the cooking time at this point. When the time is up, turn the heat off, but leave the lid on tightly for a few more minutes, to loosen the grain from the bottom of the pot. **These proportions should be used when making one of our recipes, which calls for a cooked grain**, to ensure the proper texture. You may like to try dextrinizing (lightly toasting in a dry skillet) some of the whole or flaked grains before boiling them. It will shorten the cooking time, and create a different, more nutty flavor, as well as making the cereal more fluffy. IF you live at over 3000 feet elevation you may need to cook the grains a little longer than the above chart indicates.

TIPS FOR CORNMEAL MUSH—In order to prevent lumps from forming, and to prevent burning, follow these few suggestions: Bring only half of the required water to a boil. Mix the other half with the cornmeal and stir this batter into the boiling water. Continue stirring it until the mixture is well thickened. It is best to use a heavy kettle for cornmeal mush. Cover and turn the heat down to low, so it will simmer gently. It is also good left over, chilled, sliced and then browned in the oven.

Loaves Casseroles & Patties

SAGE

BASIL

THYME

PARSLEY

TARRAGON

MINT

ROSEMARY

GARLIC

LOAVES, CASSEROLES AND PATTIES

We present here some delicious and fairly simple main dishes that you may like to include in your menus from time to time. We would encourage you, however, to **learn** to use and enjoy **most frequently the simplest dishes:** baked potatoes, corn on the cob, a pot of well cooked, nicely seasoned beans, etc. These require the least work and impart even better nutrition, than more complex dishes. If prepared carefully, and served with eye appeal and other complimentary dishes, **simple** main dishes will be enjoyed by the whole family.

GARBANZO LOAF
(or Sandwich Meat)

Yield: 1½ quarts

1¼ c dry garbanzos (soak overnight in 3 c water and drain)	3 cloves fresh garlic
¾ c sunflower seeds	1 t EACH paprika and celery salt
1 lg onion OR 2 t onion powder	1½ T starch
1 T CHICKEN STYLE SEASONING, OR 1½ T soy sauce	¼ c yeast flakes (opt.)
	⅓ c lemon juice
	3½ c hot water

Blenderize all until creamy. Will need to blend in 3 portions, if using a regular blender, with some of the liquid in each part. Bake in a greased narrow loaf pan or on a cookie sheet (if you wish to cut squares later for sandwich meat). Bake the loaf for 45–60 minutes at 350° F. Serve fresh from oven, or cool and slice, or may brown slices later in a nonstick skillet.

MILLET LOAF

4¼ c tomato juice OR blenderized tomatoes	½ t celery salt
1 med onion, chopped OR 2 t onion powder	⅓ t EACH, rubbed sage and savory
⅔ c raw sunflower seed, sesame seed OR cashews	½ c chopped olives OR chopped nuts
	1 c uncooked millet
	1 t salt (less if tomatoes are salted)

Blenderize all but millet and olives in 1 cup of the tomato juice. Combine with the olives and millet, in a nonstick or heavy saucepan (to prevent burning). Cover, bring to a boil, turn heat very low and simmer for 45 min. to 1 hr. Serve as is, in a pretty casserole dish, garnished with a little green, or chill and slice for sandwich cold-cuts.

SUN BURGERS

Yield: 1 dozen

2½ c cooked brown rice	½ c boiling water
1½ c grated raw carrot (packed)	1 sm onion, chopped
½ c rolled oats	½ c sunflower seeds
¼ t salt (more if rice is not salted)	⅓ t EACH, rubbed sage and celery salt

Place the items in the left column in a mixing bowl. Blenderize the water and the other ingredients listed in the right column, until creamy. Mix this creamy mixture with the other items in a bowl. Place by ⅓ c portions on a cookie sheet. Press out into a burger shape with a fork. Bake at 400° F. for abut 40 minutes or until a little crispy around the edges. Good with lettuce or sprouts on an open-face sandwich.

SOY SOUFFLE

Yield: 1 quart dish

1 c water

1 c tomatoes OR 1 c water
      incl. 2 T lemon juice

1½ c soaked soybeans (soak ¾ c
      dry beans overnight)

¼ c sunflower seeds

2 t CHICKEN STYLE SEASONING
      OR 1 T soy sauce

¼ t EACH celery salt, sweet basil and salt

½ t onion powder

⅓ c cornmeal OR flour

Blenderize all but the cornmeal to a cream, then stir in the meal. Will need to blend half at a time. Place in a greased, floured casserole dish. Bake at 350° F. for abut 45 minutes. May add sliced spinach without the tomato, or sliced celery with the tomato, for a change.

SPINACH QUICHE

Yield: 1 pie, 4 servings

1½ c cold water

1½ c soaked, drained soybeans

2 T lemon juice

2 T CHICKEN STYLE SEASONING

2 T raw sunflower seeds

1½ t onion powder

¼ t EACH, garlic powder and celery salt

2 T starch OR 3 T flour

2 c raw, finely sliced spinach

Blenderize all but spinach until it is very creamy and light (one full minute). Pour it in a bowl, stir in the spinach, then place it in an unbaked pie crust (the sides of the pie crust should not be too high, as they will burn easily), or if you prefer, just bake it as a souffle in a greased casserole dish. Plain bread dough is very nice for a vegetable dish crust. Roll it thinly and let it rise a little before baking. Place the pie dish on a cookie sheet to prevent burning. Bake at 375° . for 45 minutes. Serve hot or warm.

LENTIL ROAST
(or Cold-cuts)

Yield: 2–4 servings

¾ c raw lentils

2 c hot water

2–3 cloves garlic

1 med onion (cut up)

¼ c raw sesame OR sunflower seeds

½ t EACH celery salt and paprika

1 t sage (rubbed)

2 T yeast flakes (opt.)

1 ¼ T soy sauce

2 T lemon juice

2½ T *Minute Tapioca*

Blenderize the dry lentils into a course flour, then add the water and other ingredients, **except** for the tapioca. When the rest of the batter is creamy, stir in the tapioca. Bake in a greased deep loaf pan for about 1½ hours at 350° F. Glass is best to prevent burning. You will need to make 2 recipes for a regular size loaf pan, but this recipe is just right for a regular blender load, therefore we write it out this way.

POTATO SALAD

Yield: about 2 quarts

8–9 med	potatoes		⅓ c	lemon juice, OR to taste
1 lg	onion, in thin chip slices		2 T	honey, OR to taste
2 stalks	celery, slice thin		1½ t	salt, OR to taste
⅓ c	sliced green onion OR parsley (opt.)		3 T	tahini
1 recipe	SUNNY SALAD DRESSING (heat on stove with ⅓ t turmeric until turns yellow)		¼ c	water

Boil and peel the potatoes. Mash half of them in the mixing bowl. Cube the rest into the bowl. Heat the **SUNNY SALAD DRESSING** with the turmeric to activate the color factor. Add this and all the other ingredients to the potato, mix well. Is best if left for a few hours so flavors will blend, and if served at room temperature rather than cold.

OAT BURGERS

Yield: 6 large burgers

2 c	water		½ t	Italian Seasoning, OR sage
2 c	lg flake rolled oats		1½ T	soy sauce
1 med	onion, chopped fine		¼ t	celery salt
1 clove	garlic, minced		½ c	nut OR seed meal (pecan OR walnut best)

Cook the onions in the water for about 5 minutes, then add the oats and cook for only 3 minutes longer. Remove from the heat, stir in the other ingredients, then place by ice cream scoopfuls on an oiled or nonstick cookie sheet. Press out with a fork. Bake at 400° F. 30 minutes, or until a little crisp around the edges. Good with tomato and lettuce and mayonnaise, on an open-faced sandwich.

MILLET PATTIES

Yield: 6–8 patties

3 c	cooked millet (packed)		1½ t	onion powder
1 c	finely chopped celery OR part bell pepper		½ t	rubbed sage
			¼ t	garlic powder
1 c	raw sunflower seed meal, sesame seed meal OR peanut meal		½ t	celery salt
½ c	ww flour			salt, if needed

Mix all the ingredients together well. Form into patties (about ½ inch thick). Bake in a nonstick, covered skillet. Brown on both sides.

RICE-NUT BAKE
(mild and delicious main dish for a fruit meal)

Yield: Serves 4

1 c	uncooked brown rice		⅛ t	turmeric (opt.)
3½ c	boiling water		¼ t	thyme
1 T	CHICKEN STYLE SEASONING OR soy sauce		⅔ c	raw, skinned peanuts OR cashews
			1 sm	onion, chopped, OR 2 t onion powder

Blenderize the nuts and seasonings in 1 c of the boiling water until creamy. Combine this with the remaining water and rice in a thick or nonstick sauce pan. Boil with lid on at a **gentle** boil for about 1 hour. Then turn it into a casserole dish and bake in a 400° F. oven until nicely browned (about 15–20 minutes). May be garnished with a few chopped nuts or parsley, etc.

PECAN LOAF

Yield: 1 small loaf

1 c pecan meal (OR walnuts)
½ c sunflower seeds
2 c cooked brown rice
3 c soft ww bread crumbs
    (lg crumbs)
½ t salt OR soy sauce to taste

⅓ t EACH, sweet basil, rubbed sage
    and celery salt
1½ c hot water
1 med onion, chopped OR 2 t onion powder
½ c ww flour

Blenderize the items in the right column until creamy. Then combine them with the other ingredients. Pack firmly into a loaf pan. Bake at 375° F. for 1¼ hours, approximately.

SPANISH RICE

Yield: Serves 3–4

4 c canned tomatoes with juice
    (cut in pieces)
1 c chopped celery (leaves too)
1 c chopped onion
⅓ c finely chopped bell pepper
1 c uncooked brown rice

½ c sliced olives, OR ⅓ c raw sunflower seeds
⅓ t cumin powder (opt.)
⅛ t oregano, OR sweet basil
1 t salt (less if tomatoes are salted)
1–2 cloves garlic, minced
1 T honey (opt.)

Combine all of these ingredients in a saucepan and bring to a boil. Cover and simmer over low heat for 1 hour. Do not stir unnecessarily. Then place in a casserole and brown lightly in a 400° F. oven.

SCALLOPED POTATOES

Yield: 2 quarts

2 c water
2 qts. thin sliced potato
1 lg onion, ring sliced
3 lg cloves garlic, minced
1 c hot water
3 T lemon juice
½ t onion powder

2 T yeast flakes
½ c raw cashews, OR sunflower seeds
¼ t thyme
1 T flour, OR starch
1½ t salt, OR to taste
2 T pimento, OR ½ t paprika

Cook the first 4 items on the left until the potatoes have turned semitransparent, but not soft. Blenderize the rest of the ingredients until **very** creamy. Drain off the water from the potatoes and blend into the blender mix. Pour the blended mix over the potatoes in an oiled casserole dish. Bake at 350° F. for 45–50 minutes. Best flavor when served fresh.

ESAU'S POTTAGE

Yield: Serves 2–4

1 c uncooked lentils
½ c uncooked brown rice
¼ t EACH, sweet basil leaf
    and rubbed sage
¼–½ c bell pepper, chopped (opt.)

1½ T soy sauce
1 med onion, chopped finely
2 cloves garlic, minced OR ¼ t garlic powder
2 T tahini
3½ c water

Mix everything together in a saucepan and simmer for about one hour or until the moisture is absorbed. It may be served as it is, garnished with parsley, or placed in a casserole and baked at 400° F. until it is lightly crusted. Makes delicious sandwiches when chilled, with tomato slices and parsley, or lettuce leaves.

BEAN BURGERS

Yield: Serves 4

3 c cooked brown rice
3 c well cooked and mashed beans(navy,
    pinto, black, kidney, sm red, etc.)
⅓ c barley or ww flour

¼ t EACH, rubbed sage and celery salt
1 t onion powder
¼ c chopped parsley OR chives (opt.)
    salt OR soy sauce to taste

Mix all ingredients together well. Form into burgers and bake at 375° F. for 25–30 minutes or until the edges are as crispy as your prefer. Good in sandwiches with tomato slices or served with gravy or just plain!

SOY-OAT PATTIES

Yield: 6–8 large patties

2 c soaked, drained soy beans
    (1 c dry beans in 2 c water)
1½ c cold water
⅓ t sweet basil herb
2 T ww flour

2 T soy sauce
1½ t onion powder
¼ t EACH, garlic powder and celery salt
1⅓ c rolled oats (stir in last)

Blenderize all the ingredients, except for the oats, until creamy. Stir in the oats and leave the batter alone for 15 minutes or longer. Bake in a covered nonstick **or** seasoned cast iron pan, with a lid on it. (A "T-Fal" chicken fryer pan is excellent for this recipe, for cooking potatoes and onions, and many other things, with no water.) Bake patties over medium heat. Brown about 5 minutes on each side. Replace the cover after turning. Good with **"TOMATO SAUCE"** or in a sandwich with a slice of tomato.

BAKED BEANS

Yield: Serves 3–6

2 c uncooked kidney, pinto OR
    other beans (see PROPORTIONS
    FOR COOKING LEGUMES)
¼ c water
1 med onion, chopped
1½ T lemon juice

2 cloves fresh garlic, minced OR ½ t garlic powder
½ t cumin powder (opt.)
    salt as desired
4 T molasses OR honey
½ c OR 6 oz. can of tomato paste
2 T flour

Cook the beans of your choice until tender, **then** add the salt and tomato paste. See the directions in **"PROPORTIONS FOR COOKING LEGUMES."** Blenderize the other seasonings with the ¼ c of water, and add this to the beans. Place in an uncovered casserole. Bake at 400° F. until the juice thickens to the consistency that you prefer (about 1 hour).

Soups, Stews and Gravies

SOUPS, STEWS AND GRAVIES

We are sharing some good soups, stews and gravies in this section of our recipes. A tasty and nutritious soup, with a crunchy or chewy type of quick bread, and a big fresh salad, make a satisfying meal. We do suggest that the soups be thicker than is customary, since the less liquid is taken with a meal, the more easily it is digested. More liquid also requires more salt.

GARBANZOS AND DUMPLINGS

Yield: Serves 4–6

8 c well cooked garbanzos and broth
    (4 c garbanzos and 4 c water) It
    takes 1½ c dry garbanzos. See
    COOKING DIRECTIONS
    FOR LEGUMES
1½ T **CHICKEN STYLE SEASONING**
    OR to taste

½ t garlic powder
2 T brewer s yeast flakes (opt.)
½ c EACH, finely chopped onion and finely
    chopped celery OR 2 t onion powder
    and ½ t celery salt
2 T tahini

Bring the cooked garbanzos and the seasonings to a rolling boil. (You should have about ½ liquid included in the 8 c.) Make one recipe of **"CORN DUMPLINGS"**. Drop these into the boiling broth and garbanzos, and cook as directed for dumplings. Makes a delicious and filling main dish. For a change, try replacing the **"CORN DUMPLINGS"** with 2 c of cooked brown rice **or** 1 c uncooked ww macaroni **OR** a recipe of **"HOMEMADE NOODLES"**.

NEW ENGLAND BOILED DINNER

sm whole potatoes OR
    quartered lg ones
sm whole carrots OR thick round slices

sm whole onions OR lg onions
    cut in lengthwise wedges
    Fresh OR frozen peas OR
    cooked garbanzos

Prepare about equal parts of each of the above items. (Less onion may be used, if you prefer.) Cook all but the green peas, with just enough water to steam-boil them effectively. When they are nearly tender, add the green peas and replace the cover for 5 minutes, or until the peas are tender. Sprinkle the vegetables with a little onion salt or soy sauce, just before serving. The idea is to combine colorful, large-cut or whole vegetables and cook them just until tender. They may be served with a sprinkle of chopped parsley or green onions also. You may choose a different combination, including summer squash, green beans or broccoli, etc.

CREAMY SPLIT PEA SOUP

Yield: about 1 quart

1¼ c uncooked split peas
4½ c water
1 bay leaf OR ⅛ t rubbed sage
2 T flour

¼ c cashew pieces OR raw sunflower seeds
½ t celery salt
1 T **CHICKEN-STYLE SEASONING OR**
    to taste
1 sm onion, chopped

Boil the first four ingredients until the split peas are very soft, about 45 minutes. Watch them carefully, because they tend to boil over **very** easily. Cool it a little and remove the bay leaf. Then blend the peas with the remaining seasonings. Simmer it until it is thick, stirring occasionally. Serve with crackers or popcorn. For color, may add ½ c small bits of carrot **after** blending the soup.

TOMATO SOUP
(may also be used as tomato gravy)

Yield: 1 quart

4 c cooked, unsalted tomatoes
    (blenderized)
½ c rolled oats OR ⅓ c flour
⅓ c cashew nuts OR other nuts OR
    sunflower seeds, etc.

1 T tahini (opt.)
½ t EACH, celery salt and regular salt
1 t onion powder
¼ t garlic powder
1 T honey (opt.)

Bring 3 c of the tomatoes to a boil, while you blenderize the remaining cup of tomatoes with the other ingredients, until the mixture is creamy. Add the mixture to the boiling tomatoes and stir-cook until it is thick. Let it simmer for 10–15 minutes, covered. Cool a little and serve. This soup is good with some type of crunchy food, such as popcorn or crackers.

BASIC CREAM-STYLE SOUP
(Notice the variations)

5 c hot water
2 c cooked brown rice
½ c cashew pieces
1½ T CHICKEN-STYLE SEASONING

1½ t onion powder
¼ t EACH, rubbed sage and garlic powder
½ t celery salt

Mix all the ingredients in a bowl. Blenderize half of this mixture at a time, so as not to overload the blender. Simmer for 15–20 minutes in a sauce pan. Remove from the heat and allow to set for ½ hour or so, before serving. Reheat a little, if necessary.

VARIATIONS—(1) "**CORN CHOWDER**": Add 1 c **EACH**, chopped potato, chopped celery and chopped onion, and 2 c cooked sweet corn. (2) "**CREAM OF PARSLEY SOUP**": Add 1–2 c fresh parsley, chopped. (3) "**CREAM OF ONION SOUP**": Add 2 medium onions, ring sliced and sauteed. (4) "**MUSHROOM-LIKE SOUP**": Add 1¼ c sliced olives. (5) For a mild **gravy**, use just plain.

CHICK PEA A LA KING

Yield: Serves 4–6

1 recipe CASHEW GRAVY
3–4 c cooked, drained garbanzos (save
    the liquid for some other use)
    salt OR onion salt, to taste
    (if garbanzos are not salted)

½ c chopped, cooked pimento OR red
    bell pepper
1 c sliced celery OR steamed green peas

Combine all the ingredients in a heavy saucepan and heat thoroughly, taking care to not burn it. Serve over hot, steamed brown rice. See "**COOKING DIRECTIONS FOR COOKING WHOLE GRAIN CEREALS**". The sauce should be quite thick and creamy. Add 1–2 T starch, if needed. Simmer for 15 minutes, approximately, to blend the flavors.

MEXICAN BEAN SOUP

Yield: Serves 5–6

6 c well cooked, unsalted black beans,
    with broth (2 c dry beans)
2½ c chopped canned tomatoes (3 c raw)
1 c chopped onion
1 c finely chopped celery (leaves also)

1 t salt OR to taste
½ t onion powder
¼ t oregano powder OR ½ t Italian seasoning
½ t cumin (opt.)
⅓ c finely chopped bell pepper

2 cloves garlic, minced   (OR more celery)

Simmer for 40 minutes. This soup is nice served with tortillas and tossed salad.

HEARTY VEGETABLE STEW

Yield: Serves 3–4

4 med Irish potatoes, cubed
½–1 c sliced celery (including leaves)
½–1 c chopped onion
      (green OR regular)
1 c diced carrot OR rutabaga
3 c water (approximately)

¾ c uncooked lentils OR ½ c raw sunflower
      seeds OR 1½ c cooked garbanzos
2 T tahini
2 cloves garlic, minced
1¼ t salt OR 1½ T soy sauce (add after tender)

Boil all the ingredients (except the salt) together in a covered pot, until tender. Then add the salt or soy sauce. Simmer some more. It has a better flavor if it is allowed to set for a little while before serving.

SPAGHETTI SAUCE
(For 8 oz of uncooked spaghetti)

Yield: 1 quart

4 c cooked tomatoes
      (chopped OR pureed)
½–1 c finely chopped onion
½–1 c sliced celery
½ c tomato paste (or more)
½ c finely chopped bell pepper
      OR ½ t paprika

2 T tahini (opt.)
⅛ t Italian seasoning OR sweet basil
2 T sweetening
2 T flour OR 1 T starch
1 t salt, if tomatoes are not salted
2 cloves garlic

Blenderize the items in the right hand column with 1 c of the cooked tomatoes. Then combine all the ingredients in a saucepan and simmer until thickened, stirring as needed. Boil the spaghetti in slightly salted water until tender. Then rinse the spaghetti under cold water, to firm it up., Serve the sauce and the spaghetti separately, or combine them in a baking dish and heat in the oven, to blend the flavors.

PIZZA SAUCE

Yield 5 cups sauce
(2 round pizzas)

1 recipe SPAGHETTI SAUCE
½ c tomato paste

¼ c flour

Mix the additional tomato paste and flour into the **"SPAGHETTI SAUCE"**. Roll out a thin crust from **"BASIC WW BREAD"**, or another bread dough. (Just make a little extra dough when baking bread.) Spread a thin layer of the warm tomato sauce on the dough, then a generous sprinkle of the **"PIZZA CHEESE"**, or **"SCRAMBLED SOYBEANS"**, **OR** use your own creativity. (A cake decorator may be used to apply the **"PIZZA CHEESE"**.) Bake at 375° F. until the edges begin to brown. For quick "mini pizzas" top regular bread slices with the above sauce and cheese and brown in the oven.

TOMATO SAUCE
(Serve over patties or loaves)

3 c cooked, unsalted tomatoes
(cut OR mash)
⅓ c EACH, finely chopped onion
(OR 1 t onion powder),
finely chopped celery, and finely
chopped green bell pepper
(OR 1 t paprika)

1 T sweetening
¼ t sweet basil OR rosemary
½ t salt
1 T starch

Combine all the ingredients in a saucepan and stir-cook until it thickens a little. Then simmer for 10 minutes or more. Good over **"SOY-OAT PATTIES"** or loaves, etc.

CASHEW GRAVY

Yield 2½ cups

2½ c water
½ t onion powder
1½ T soy sauce OR CHICKEN-STYLE
SEASONING OR just salt to taste

½ c raw cashew pieces
2–3 T barley flour, OR rice flour OR oat flour

Blenderize ½ c of the water with all the other ingredients until very creamy. Bring the other 2 c of water to a boil and add the blended mixture to this, as you stir. Simmer for 5 minutes and serve. It is excellent over potatoes.

COUNTRY-STYLE GRAVY

½ c dextrinized oat flour OR ww flour
—oat flour is best (to dextrinize,
toast lightly in a dry skillet)
⅓ c nuts (cashew, pecan, sunflower
seeds)

2 T soy sauce OR to taste
3 c water
¼ t EACH, celery salt, rubbed sage and
garlic powder
1 sm onion, chopped OR 2 t onion powder

Place 2 c of the water in a sauce pan and bring to a boil. Blenderize the remaining water with the other ingredients until it is very smooth. Pour this into the boiling water as you stir constantly, until it thickens. Turn the heat low, cover and cook for about 10–15 minutes.

CHICKEN-STYLE GRAVY

3 c water
pinch of turmeric (opt.)
½ t onion powder
1 T CHICKEN-STYLE SEASONING
OR to taste

⅓ c cashew pieces
¼ c barley flour, OR rice flour OR oat flour
2 T brewer's yeast flakes (opt.)

Bring 2 cups of the water to a boil. Blenderize the other ingredients in the remaining 1 cup of water. Pour this into the boiling water, stirring constantly. After it thickens, simmer for 10 minutes. Serve over rice, loaves, patties or potatoes.

PEANUT BUTTER GRAVY

Yield: 3 cups

3 c water
⅓ c peanut butter OR ½ c
    toasted peanuts
⅓ c rice flour OR barley flour OR
    other flour

½ t celery salt
1 t salt
¼ t garlic powder
1 t onion powder

Bring 2 c of the above water to a rolling boil. While this is heating, blenderize the remaining cup of water with the flour and other ingredients until creamy. Pour this into the boiling water while stirring. Cook, stirring constantly, until it thickens. Cover and simmer for about 15 minutes. This gravy is especially good on boiled or baked potatoes.

COOKING DIRECTIONS FOR LEGUMES

Boiled or baked legumes can be a nutritious and delicious part of the diet. They contain high quality protein, carbohydrates, fats, vitamins, minerals and fiber. The most common complaint from consumers is that they cause flatulence or gas. So the first thing is to learn how to cook them thoroughly.

For 1 Cup Dry Legumes	Water	Boiling Time	Salt or Seasoning
Navy beans, Pinto beans,	3 c	3–4 hours, or	½ t salt per c of dry
Great northern beans, Black		overnight in the	beans, or other
beans, Red beans, Lima beans,		Crock-pot, on medium	seasoning such as
Kidney beans, Etc.		or high.	unfermented soy
			sauce or **"Chicken-Style Seasoning"**, etc.
Garbanzos or Soybeans.	4 c	5–6 hours, or overnight on high in a Crock-pot. Best if pressure-cooked.	Same as above.
Lentils or Split peas.	3 c	1½–2 hours.	Same as above.

GENERAL DIRECTIONS—Sort and wash the beans. Then cook the beans in the required amount of water overnight, **or** bring the beans to a boil in the required amount of water, turn the heat off, and allow to soak for 1 hour or more with the lid on. If you use **both** of these soaking methods you will shorten the cooking time even more. Boil the beans for the length of time shown on the above chart. Do **not** add salt, onion or other seasoning, until the beans are very tender, as this will lengthen the cooking time. Soft water also hastens the cooking. Sliced or chopped onion and some minced garlic are delicious with legumes. Simmer the beans for a while after adding the seasonings, to blend the flavors. Split peas tend to boil over very easily, as well as soybeans, so watch them very closely. If you live at an elevation over 3000 feet, you may want to cook the legumes longer than the above chart indicates.

PRESSURE COOKING LEGUMES—A 6–9 quart pressure cooker (for the average-sized family) is a real time and energy saver! After soaking the beans as directed above, place them directly into the pressure cooker, without the rack. Most beans require about 30–40 minutes, and soybeans and garbanzos take about 50–60 minutes (with the petcock rocking gently). Start timing when the gauge starts to rock. When the time is up, take the pressure cooker over to the sink carefully, and run a little cold water over it to lower the pressure quickly. If the beans are soft, add the seasoning and simmer to blend the flavors, then serve. **Do**

not pressure split peas, as they may clog the air vent and cause a big mess. To prevent soybeans or lima bean skins from stopping up the vent, you may want to cut out a round of wire screen and mold it into a dome-shape to fit over the beans (inside the pressure cooker); **or** place the beans in a deep stainless steel bowl, pour an inch of water in the cooker, and then place the bowl in the cooker.

PRESSURE CANNING LEGUMES—Sort legumes, removing the bad ones and foreign objects. **Rinse** them in a strainer. **Measure** 1¼ cup dry beans for each quart of cooked beans desired (a 21 quart pressure canner will hold four 2 quart jars or seven 1 quart jars). Place the rinsed beans in jars and fill with water to 1 ½ inch below top of jar and **soak overnight**. Cover with a new lid and screw the lid on securely. Pour about 2 quarts of hot water in the pressure canner, followed by the jars of beans. Place the lid on the canner and tighten, with the **petcock open**. Bring to a boil and allow the **steam to escape for 10 minutes**. Close the petcock and keep close watch on the pressure gauge.

Begin timing when the pressure reaches **10–15 lbs.** Turn the heat down to medium or medium-low, to **maintain this pressure** (higher altitudes require a little more pressure than lower ones). It should take **1 hour** in a pressure canner at 10–15 lbs. for most beans, but closer to 1½ **hours** for garbanzos or soybeans to cook thoroughly. The bean skins, as well as the insides, should be tender.

When the time is up, turn the heat off and allow the pressure to come down naturally (quick cooling may break the jars, or cause the contents to boil out of them). When the pressure is down to 1 lb., it is safe to open the petcock. After opening the petcock, leave lid ajar a little for 5 minutes, then open the lid on the cooker and carefully lift the jars out onto a dishtowel or newspaper to cool When cool, check for seal, and store, as you would other canned goods.

Desserts

DESSERTS

We all enjoy desserts, and they **can** be healthful! Nice ripe, succulent fruit makes a wonderful dessert as one of the main dishes at a fruit meal. The following desserts are delicious, though not as sweet as the traditional variety. They are sweetened mainly with sweet fruit, such as banana, dates, or pineapple juice. A small amount of honey is used in some recipes, but may be omitted in most of them. We encourage all to use **these simple desserts** as a (1) **main dish**, an (2) **additional bread**, or as a (3) **spread**, to be placed on the table at the time the rest of the meal is served. One can enjoy a large piece of a truly healthful pie, as a main part of the meal, for example, without worrying about excess calories. A birthday dinner can be just as health building, as any other meal! Desserts for both fruit and vegetable meals are included.

JIFFY PUMPKIN PIE

Yield: One 9 inch pie

¾ c hot water
¾ c raw cashews OR ⅔ c soymilk powder
¼ c honey and 1 T Grandma's
    Molasses OR ½ c *Sucanat*
2 t vanilla

1¼ t CINNAMON SUBSTITUTE
¾ t salt
2 T plain *Emes* gelatin, dissolved in
    ½ c boiling water
2 c solid pack pumpkin (16 oz. can)

Sprinkle *Emes* gelatin into ½ c boiling water, in a saucepan, cover and leave alone for a few minutes. Place all but the pumpkin in the blender and blend until very smooth. Heat pumpkin until pretty warm, in the saucepan you just used for the *Emes* gelatin. Add as much of the warmed pumpkin to the blended mix as you can and stir in the rest by hand thoroughly. Clean all of the pie mix out of the blender into a prebaked pie shell. Chill to set *Emes* gelatin. This pie filling can be baked in a pie shell if you prefer a darker look, but it has a good flavor without baking. Libby's brand pumpkin has a good flavor. Some brands we have tried have a metallic flavor. If you don't have *Emes* gelatin, you may thicken pie with 3½ T food starch, but you will need to stir continuously as you thicken it over heat.

PIÑA COLADA PUDDING

Yield: over 2 quarts

9 c liquid (46 oz. can pineapple juice
    and water to make 9 c)
1⅓ c raw millet grain
1½ t salt
½ c coconut

½ c cashews OR blanched almonds
½ c soymilk powder
1½ t vanilla
1 t lemon extract
2 T honey

Cook the items in the left column for at least 35–40 minutes with lid on saucepot. Best to use a heavy kettle, so it won't scorch. Then stir in the flavorings on the right, briskly with a wire whisk. Now, while mix is hot blenderize portions of it until very creamy. Pour at once into pudding cups or other mold. For a variation place dried prunes, apricots or peaches on the bottom of the dish before pouring hot pudding in, or place pudding in a glass casserole and top with thickened blueberries or strawberries. Chill and serve. Needs to cool **uncovered** or it won't gel properly!

FRUIT POPSICLES

To make banana Popsicles, cut ripe bananas in half, put them on Popsicle sticks or forks and freeze thoroughly. They may be dipped in carob sauce (or something else) just before serving. Try some of the following ideas to make simple summer treats, using Popsicle molds: (1) Blenderized fruit combinations, such as, banana-pineapple, peach-strawberry or orange-peach. (2) Any fruit juice (3) Canned fruit, blenderized. These should not be used as in-between-meal snacks, but just before or after a meal. If eaten slowly, they will not chill the stomach. Our digestive systems need complete rest between meals, if they are to keep a healthy tone.

CAROB PUDDING OR PIE

Yield: one 9 inch Pie

1 c boiling water	1 t *Postum* OR *Pero* (opt.)
2½ T *Emes* plain gelatin	⅓ c *Sucanat* OR ¼ c honey
2 c cold water	¾ t salt
1 c walnuts OR cashews	2 t vanilla
½ c carob powder	

Dissolve the *Emes* gelatin in the boiling water and set aside. Blenderize all the other ingredients in the 2 cups of cold water until very creamy. Add all of the gelatin mix into the blender mix and blend a little more to mix thoroughly. Pour into prebaked pie crust **or** pudding cups. Chill and serve. If you don't have the *Emes* gelatin, you may thicken the pie over the stove with 3½ T starch dissolved in a little water.

NUTTY CAROB FUDGE

2 lg bananas, must be ripe to be sweet enough for recipe	pinch of salt
	¼ c carob powder
½ c peanut butter	1 c roasted peanuts (may use other nuts,
1 t vanilla	but best with peanuts)

Peel and mash the bananas with a fork on a plate until creamy. Cream in the peanut butter and flavorings until thoroughly mixed. May use a bowl, but not necessary. Place the peanuts on the bottom of a bread pan and top with the carob cream. Smooth a little. Freeze overnight. You now want to quickly cut this big bar into squares and refreeze in a tight plastic bag to ensure freshness, unless it will all be used immediately. A little warm water running over the bottom of the pan will loosen the fudge bar so you can cut it up on a cutting board with a butcher knife.

BANANA CREAM PIE

Yield: 1 pie filling

2 c water	1 t vanilla
½ c raw cashews OR other mild nuts	½ c pitted dates, chopped
⅓ t salt	3 T starch OR 4 T flour

Blenderize 1 c of the water with all the other ingredients until creamy. Add the other cup of water and stir-cook in a saucepan until it is very thick. Partially cool, then spread a thin layer of this cream in a prebaked pie shell. Place a layer of fresh, ripe, sliced bananas on top of this, then another layer of the cream and repeat. Finish off with a little of the cream. Fill the crust up, or even heap it up a little. Chill and serve the same day or the following day. It may be decorated, just before serving, with freshly cut banana slices or chopped nuts.

FRESH BERRY PIE
(peaches may also be used)

Yield: one 9 inch pie

2 c fresh berries OR other soft
     fruit (packed)
1 T honey (opt.)

pinch of salt
¾ c pineapple juice OR other sweet juice
3 T starch

Blenderize the above items together until smooth. Stir-cook in a saucepan until thick. When partially cooled, use this glaze as a binder between layers of freshly sliced strawberries, peaches or whole blueberries, raspberries, etc. (**about 4–5 cups**). Layer this into a prebaked pie shell. Use plenty of fresh fruit of the same kind as you used for the glaze, until the pie is rounded up a little. Chill and serve as it is or with some kind of whipped cream. (See our cream and pie crust recipes.) Serve a large piece of pie to each person, as it is much like a fruit salad.

BASIC FRUIT PIE FILLING

Yield; 1 generous pie

5 c fresh apples, peaches OR berries,
     sliced OR cubed (about 1
     heaping pie pan full) OR 3½
     c cooked chunky fruit
¾ c sweet fruit juice (only ½ c for soft
     fruitlike berries OR peaches).
     Use part juice concentrate,
     if a sweeter pie is desired

¼ t salt
1—2 T honey (opt.)
1 t vanilla
2 T starch OR 3 T *Minute Tapioca*
1 t CINNAMON SUBSTITUTE
    (for apple pie only)

If using fresh apples or pears, simmer the fruit with the juice until it starts to become tender. Then add the thickening and flavorings and turn it into an unbaked pie crust and bake. If using peaches or berries, which are already soft, just combine the **juice** and thickener and stir-cook until thick, then add the fruit and flavorings. Turn into the unbaked crust and bake. If using **cooked chunky or sliced fruit**, add **no juice**, but only the thickening agent and flavorings, since the fruit is already soft. Fresh fruit provides the best texture quality for pies, but canned fruit may be substituted when the other is not available.

PINEAPPLE RICE

Yield: about 5 cups

3 c well cooked brown rice
2½ c crushed or chunky pineapple (#2 can)
1 t vanilla

¼ t salt (more if needed)
½ c soymilk powder
½ c chopped nuts (opt.)

Directions: Mix all ingredients together thoroughly. Chill and serve. Add a little honey if it is not sweet enough to suit you. Dole brand is often sweeter than other brands, as some are not ripe.

APPLE-OAT PIE CRUST
(a non-rich press-in type crust)

Yield: 1 bottom crust
Prebaked Crust

1 full c oat flour OR 1¼ c quick oats   ½ c smooth applesauce
¼ t salt

Mix in a bowl quickly. **Press at once into a pie pan**, starting with the sides. It will be sticky, but hands are washable! Bake at 350° F. for 20–25 minutes or until lightly browned. Fill the crust the night before or at least several hours before serving, and chill, as this will soften the crust. **Loosen the edges** of the crust before cutting, or removing with a pie server.

LEMON PIE

Yield: 1 pie filling

3 c pineapple juice   ⅓ t salt
⅓ c water   2 t lemon juice
½ c uncooked millet OR 5 T starch ½ t lemon extract
⅓ c shredded coconut   1 T honey (opt.)
¼ c raw cashew nuts OR
        blanched almonds

If using millet as the thickener, combine it with the water, nuts and pineapple juice in a saucepan. Cover and boil gently for 35 minutes. If it boils too vigorously, too much liquid will be lost by evaporation. Place this in the blender while hot, add all the other ingredients and blenderize until very creamy. Pour at once into a prebaked pie shell or pudding cups, and chill uncovered until it sets. If you are using starch to thicken it, omit the ⅓ cup of water, blend the remaining items together for 1 full minute and stir-cook in a saucepan until thick. Pour into a prebaked pie crust and chill.

WHEAT-OAT PIE CRUST
(good roll-out type)

Yield: 1 double crust

1 c nuts (any rich kind)   ½ t salt
1 c ww flour (soft)   ⅓ c cold water
½ c rolled oats

Blenderize the ingredients in the left column until fine, using rubber spatula to push flours off sides as it blends. Place flour mix in bowl and combine thoroughly with the ⅓ c water, but do not knead more than necessary. Divide dough in half and roll out evenly between wax paper. If the filling is hot when placed between the crust, the pie should bake at 350° F. in about 45 minutes. Turn heat down toward end if necessary.

"GRAHAM CRACKER" PIE CRUST
(good press-in type)

Yield: single crust

⅔ c millet flour   ½ t salt
⅓ c rice flour   ¼ c cold water
½ c pecan meal (OR other
        rich tasting nuts)

Blenderize all the items in the left column until very finely ground. Add the cold water all at once and stir in with spoon thoroughly. It will be on the sticky side, so let it set a few minutes as you get your pie plate out and pour some warm water in a little bowl. If you dip your fingers in the warm water you can quickly press the pie crust in place, beginning with the edges. Be sure to leave the upper edge thick enough so it won't burn. Bake at 350° for 25–30 minutes. Watch carefully near end of this time. Good for a prebaked crust.

EASY OAT PIE CRUST
(press-in type crust)

Yield: single crust

1¼ c quick oats
⅓ c shredded coconut (unsweetened)
¼ t salt

1 T ww flour
⅓ c cold water

Blenderize about half of the oats with the flour, salt and coconut until fine. Mix this in a bowl with the rest of the oats and water quickly and well. Turn it into a greased pie plate. Moisten fingers in water and work quickly to press out crust evenly, beginning with the sides. It becomes more sticky the longer you work with it. Bake at 350° F. for about 30 minutes. Fill with the precooked filling of your choice.

CARROT MACAROON COOKIES

2 c pineapple with its juice
1 c rolled oats
¾ t salt
¼ c honey OR less

1 t vanilla
2½ c raw carrot, grated med-fine
1 c unsweetened macaroon OR
        shredded coconut
½ c cornmeal

Blenderize the items on the left until creamy. Place this in a bowl and stir in the other three ingredients. Drop by spoonfuls on an oiled cookie sheet. Bake at 375° F. for 35–40 minutes or until they start to brown a little around the edges.

CAROB CAKE

Yield: 9 inch layer

½ c quick oats
1½ c ww flour (hard)
½ c carob powder
2 t *Pero* OR *Postum* (opt.)
¾ t salt

⅓ c sesame tahini
1¾ c very warm water (OR 1⅓ c cold
        water with HP*)
3–4 T honey OR 5 T *Sucanat*
½ t vanilla
2 T *Ener-G* baking powder* (or ¼ c HP*)

Mix the ingredients in the left column in a bowl very thoroughly, to cream in the tahini. Then mix in the moist items, but leave the baking powder or HP until last. Oven should be preheated. Mix in the baking powder quickly and evenly with a wire whisk, and turn batter into a greased cake pan. Bake for about 40 minutes at 375° F.—less for cup cakes. *See note under **"LEMON COOKIES"**.

See Hydrogen Peroxide or Ener-G baking powder information under "SPECIAL TERMS AND INGREDIENTS"

LEMON COOKIES

Yield: 1 dozen medium

1 c millet flour
¾ c rice flour
¼ c barley flour (OR ww)
½ c shredded coconut
½ c cashews OR blanched almonds
¾ t salt

½ t vanilla
1 T honey
1 t lemon extract
1¼ c warm pineapple juice (OR 1 scant
    cup cold juice with HP*)
1¾ T *Ener-G* baking powder* (OR ⅓ c HP*)

Blenderize the coconut and cashews with the millet flour until very fine. Mix all but the baking powder together in a bowl. Have oven hot. Mix in the baking powder or HP quickly and evenly with a wire whisk. Place by spoonful in desired size on a nonstick cookie sheet and bake at 375° F. for 25–30 minutes.

*See Hydrogen Peroxide or Ener-G baking powder information under "SPECIAL TERMS AND INGREDIENTS"

SWEET POTATO COOKIES

3 c cooked sweet potato, mashed
    (on the dry side)
3 T molasses OR 1 c crushed
    pineapple + 2 T honey

½ c ww flour OR oat flour
1 t vanilla
½ t salt
½ c nuts (any kind)

Blenderize flour and nuts until finely ground. Mix all items together well. Form into walnut-sized balls; then flatten nicely with fork. You may roll them in coconut first. Bake at 400° F. for 35–40 minutes or until lightly browned. Serve hot or cold. They are not a rich cookie, but good, and colorful!

OATMEAL FRUIT COOKIES

Yield: 1–2 dozen

1½ c ripe banana, mashed OR
    mashed persimmon, blended
    pineapple OR applesauce, etc.
1¼ c quick oats
2 T ww flour

½ c nut meal, any kind
½ c chopped dates OR raisins
1 t fresh orange rind, grated OR ½ t
    orange extract OR other extract
1 t vanilla
⅓ t salt.

Mix all the ingredients together thoroughly, in a bowl. Place the batter by spoonfuls, on an oiled or nonstick cookie sheet. Bake at 375° F. for 23–35 minutes. If a richer cookie is desired, use a sweet type of fruit sauce (banana versus applesauce), and add ¼ c chopped nuts in addition to the nut meal. You may create many varieties of cookies, by simply changing the kind of fruit sauce used, and the flavorings. Persimmon and banana are two of our favorites, made with chopped dates.

FRUIT CAKE

3 c smooth applesauce
    (OR part mashed banana)
2 c crushed pineapple
    (partially drained)
1 c chopped dates
1 c raisins
1 c chopped apricots
1 c chopped pecans OR walnuts

1 c nuts (for meal)
1½ t salt
2 t vanilla
1½ T grated orange rind
2 T honey (opt.)
1 c quick oats
½ c ww flour
¾ c cornmeal

Blenderize the last cup of nuts with the cornmeal until finely ground. Mix all the ingredients together thoroughly in a bowl. Turn into a greased and floured Bundt or flat cake pan and smooth the top.

Bake at 350° F. for 1¼ hours. It is best to place the cake pan on a cookie sheet to prevent burning. A thin coating of liquid lecithin and oil prevents the cake from sticking to the pan (better than other oils or shortening). Cool the cake in the pan, so that it will not break while you are removing it from the pan.

BANANA CAROB DROP COOKIES

Yield: 1 dozen large cookies

1 ½ c ripe bananas, mashed (3–4 bananas)
½ c EACH, soy flour, ww flour and
      rolled oats
¼ c carob flour

⅓ c nuts
1 t vanilla
½ t salt
1 T honey

Blenderize the nuts with soy flour and ww flour until finely ground. Mash the bananas, then combine all the other ingredients with them, adding the oats last, so as not to break them up so much. Place the batter, by spoonfuls, on an oiled or nonstick cookie sheet. Bake for 35–45 minutes at 375° F. Cool and serve.

FRUIT ICE CREAMS

A variety of delicious, soft, fruit-based ice creams may be made in a regular blender. For a family of two, four or six, this is very satisfactory. For feeding a large group, you really need a "Champion Juicer" or at least an institutional-size blender such as "Vita-Mix".

Put about 1 cup of fruit juice **or** milk (soy, nut or other(in the blender. While the blades are whirling, add sliced, **frozen** banana until the mixture becomes thick. A little vanilla may be added.

To make a good fruit sherbet, try some of the following combinations, using the method described above: (1) Frozen cantaloupe and pineapple juice (2) Frozen strawberries, frozen bananas and pineapple **or** orange juice.

For carob ice cream, put 1 cup of rich nut milk **or** soy milk in the blender. Add a little carob powder (try 2 T), vanilla and enough thinly sliced **frozen** bananas to make a soft ice cream.

If you make a small amount at once, you can make it quite thick, without damaging the blender motor. You may want to place it in the freezer for an hour before the meal, to harden it a little. If it stays too long, it will become too hard, since it is not half "fat", like most ice cream! If it is eaten slowly, so that it is warmed up in the mouth, it will not greatly retard digestion. Bananas are probably the favorite fruit, to use by themselves, or in combination with other fruits, because of their creamy texture and sweet flavor. Ripe bananas may be bought in large quantities when on sale, peeled and then frozen in tight plastic bags. If the freezer is cold enough, they will retain their light color. Spoiled bananas should never be used, but they should be somewhat speckled before being frozen. Partially green bananas are less digestible and less sweet than well ripened ones.

SOY CHEESE CAKE

Yield: one 10 inch round cake pan

2 c pineapple juice
1½ c soaked soybeans (3/4 c dry)
1 T lemon juice
1 c cashews OR blanched almonds
1 t salt

2 T honey
1½ t lemon extract
1 t vanilla
½ c millet flour OR 3 T starch

Parboil the soaked soybeans for 1 minute, drain and cool them in cold water and drain again. Blend the nuts with 1 cup of the juice until creamy. Blend the beans with the remaining ingredients, except the millet flour, with the other cup of pineapple juice, until creamy. Then combine everything in a bowl and mix well. Pour into a greased and floured heavy cake pan or pie plate. Bake at 350° F. for about 1 hour. Delicious!

QUICK RAISIN CAKE
(or muffins)

Yield: 9 inch layer

1¼ c **hard ww flour**
⅓ c **quick oats**
½ c **rice flour (OR cornmeal)**
½ c **shredded coconut**
¼ c **tahini**
¾ t **salt**

1½ c **very warm pineapple juice (OR**
      1 c cold juice with HP*)
1 T **honey**
1½ t **vanilla**
⅔ c **raisins (OR chopped dates)**
2 T *Ener-G* **baking powder* (OR ⅓ c HP*)**

Preheat the oven. Blenderize the ww flour with the coconut until fine. Place in a bowl and mix in the other flours, creaming thoroughly with the tahini. Mix in the juice and other items, except for the baking powder. Grease and flour baking pan. Mix in the baking powder well with a wire whisk. Bake at 375° F. for about 35 minutes—less for muffins.

*See Hydrogen Peroxide or Ener-G baking powder information under "Special Terms and Ingredients"

BASIC CAKE RECIPE
(yeast-raised)

2 c **very warm, sweet fruit juice**
1 T **sweetening**
1 T **active yeast**
1 t **vanilla extract**

2¾ c **ww flour**
½ c **oat flour (make in blender)**
½ c **nuts**
1 t **salt**

Blend the nuts with some of the flour until very fine. Dissolve the sweetening in the warm juice and sprinkle the yeast into it.1 Leave alone until the yeast foams up a little. Then stir in the flours, nut meal, vanilla and salt and **follow the variation of your choice**, from those listed. Read the whole recipe before beginning to mix anything. When the batter is ready for the oven, place it in a round, square or tube baking pan. Let it rise in a warm place for 8–10 minutes. Preheat the oven and bake at 400° F. for 15 minutes. Reduce the heat to 350° F. and bake for 25–35 minutes longer. Be sure it is well baked. Cool on a rack and store in a cool place, but preferably not in the refrigerator. Use within the next two days, otherwise you **should** keep it in cold storage. Makes a delicious, healthful and satisfying treat! You may like to frost it (just before serving) with **"COCONUT CREAM"**, **"CAROB SAUCE"** or **"LEMON SAUCE"**.

CAKE VARIATIONS: (1) **Simple Fruit Cake**—Add to the above, 2 c chopped, dried fruit of your choice, ½ c chopped nuts and 2 t finely grated orange rind. (2) **Banana Cake**—Add 2 ripe bananas, cut in cubes, 1 t grated orange rind and 2 T honey (opt.) (3) **Carob Cake**—Use apple juice **or** grape juice for the liquid called for in the basic recipe,. After the yeast has foamed up, use a portion of this yeast water to blend the following in: 1 c chopped, pitted dates, ½ c carob powder, and ½ c cashews or pecans or walnuts. **Then** stir together with the rest of the liquid, flour, etc., as the basic recipe calls for. (4) **Plain Raisin Cake**—Add 1½ c raisins and 1 t **"CINNAMON SUBSTITUTE"** to the basic cake batter.

The **"CAROB CAKE"** may be sliced in three layers with a bread knife and filled between the layers with sliced banana, then frosted with **"COCONUT CREAM"** or another frosting. The **"BANANA CAKE"** may be sliced in this way, filled with layers of sliced, ripe bananas and frosted with **"CAROB-NUT ICING"** or **"BANANA CAROB SAUCE"**. Have fun using your imagination! Try some other fruit fillings, etc.

MILKS, CREAMS, SAUCES AND "CHEESES"

The following recipes are made from cooked grains, cooked legumes, and/or nuts. Thus they combine the good flavor of nuts with the creamy texture, low cost and easy digestibility of well cooked legume and/or whole grain. The milk recipes are purposely on the creamy side, as they taste richer and add less liquid to the meal. As dairy product allergies are becoming more frequent, and the fear of contracting disease from animals is well founded by scientific studies, we share the following recipes which we have found delightful. Try your own creativity. You may come up with something you like better. Learn to use your blender properly for the best texture, and try to avoid waste by using a good, supple, rubber spatula when removing food from the blender.

BASIC SOY MILK

Yield: 1 quart

1 c dry soybeans (soak these overnight
      in about 4 c cold water)
⅓ t salt

1 t vanilla (opt.)
1 T sweetening (opt.)
3 c hot water

Sort the dry beans before soaking overnight. Drain them and add enough fresh water to cover them. Bring them to a boil (tends to boil over, so watch), turn heat down and boil for **5 minutes**. Drain and cool beans with cold water, to prevent strong flavor. Now blend about half of the beans with half of the water for only about 30 seconds. Repeat with the other half portion. Strain this slurry through a fine fruit jelly strainer bag, or other fine cloth (nylon is best for strength). It works well for the strainer bag or cloth to rest in a large wire sieve over a catching container. A homemade press could be made for this procedure, if you like to make it often. Return this milk to a clean blender and blend in the flavors thoroughly. Chill milk in cold water or refrigerator. The soybean pulp may be used for making crackers, patties or may be added to bread, as it still contains good nutrients and fiber.

SOY/NUT-GRAIN MILK

Yield: 1 quart

1½ c boiling water
½ c cashew pieces OR other
      nuts or ½ c soymilk powder

1 c well cooked rice
¼ t salt OR to taste
1–2 t honey

Blenderize the above ingredients until very creamy; then add 1–1½ c additional cold water (the amount depends on how creamy you prefer it). This milk is intended for a cereal topping, rather than a beverage. Chill and serve, or heat and serve hot over toast. For banana milk, add 2–4 ripe bananas and ½ t vanilla.

RICE MILK

Yield: 3 cups

1 c well cooked brown rice
1¼ c boiling water
3 T cashew nut pieces OR
      other light nuts

2 t honey
¼ t salt
1½ c additional water, cold

Blenderize all but the cold water, to a cream. Add the cold water while it is still blending. Chill or serve at once. For carob milk, just add: 3 T carob flour, ½ t vanilla and a little more honey. It will taste sweeter if cold, than when hot, but is good both ways.

CAROB MILK

Yield: 1 quart

3½ c water, part OR all boiling hot
⅓ c pitted, chopped dates (packed)
⅛ t salt

½ c cashew pieces OR blanched almonds
½ t vanilla extract
2 T carob powder, OR to taste

Blenderize 1 c of boiling water with all other ingredients until smooth and creamy. Add remainder of the water, either cold or hot. This is a good a hot drink, but will taste sweeter when cold.

SOY WHIPPED CREAM

Yield: 2½ cups

2 c cold water
¾ c soymilk powder
2½ T *Instant Clear Gel*
1–2 T light honey

¼ t salt
1½ t vanilla
2 t lemon juice (stir in last by hand)

Blenderize all but the lemon until very creamy and quite thick, then stir in the lemon juice by hand. **You may substitute 1 cup of blanched almonds for the soymilk** and add a little more salt. This will make a whiter cream than the soymilk will.

CASHEW WHIPPED CREAM

Yield: 3 cups

2¾ c water
1 T EACH, starch and flour
    (barley or white)
2 T honey OR 6–8 chopped, pitted dates

1 c raw cashew pieces
1½ t vanilla extract
½ t salt

Bring 2 c of the water to a boil, while you blenderize the other ingredients in the remaining ¾ c of water, until very creamy. Pour this into the boiling water while stirring constantly. Stir-cook until thickened nicely. Chill and serve, as you would any whipped cream.

COCONUT CREAM
(or frosting)

Yield: about 3 cups

2 ½ c shredded coconut
2¼ c cold water
½ t salt
2 T honey

2 t vanilla (OR half lemon extract)
2 t lemon juice
2 ½ T *Instant Clear Gel*

Thoroughly dry out and heat the coconut in a dry pan over a low heat, but do not brown it. Stir almost constantly. Put at once while still warm in blender and blend into butter, by pushing coconut gently off sides into center (watch your spatula). Blend in all other ingredients until very creamy. Chill and serve. If using cream as a frosting, add more *Instant Clear Gel* (for desired thickness).

FRUIT SAUCES
(or canned fruit)

Canned or frozen fruit, blenderized until very creamy, or used as it is, makes a very nice alternate for milk, to be used over dry or cooked cereals. Fruit nectar or fruit juice is also delicious used in this way. Many home canned fruits, if ripe when processed, have a delicious flavor without additional sweetening. Unsweetened canned fruit may also be found at the grocery store.

APPLE CREAM

Yield: 2½ cups

½ c cold water
1 t vanilla
⅛ t salt
⅓ c raw cashews OR blanched
     almonds

2 t EACH honey and lemon juice
3 lg raw yellow delicious apples
     (peeled and cubed)

Blenderize in the order given until smooth and creamy. Make just before serving the meal. Is nice over fruit salad, fruit pie or **QUICK RAISIN CAKE**, etc.

BANANA CAROB SAUCE

Yield: 1½ cups

3 lg bananas, ripe
⅓ c smooth peanut butter
     OR other pure nut butter

2–2½ T carob powder
½ t vanilla

Blend just before serving, since the banana will oxidize if left for very long. Cut up the ripe bananas into the blender first. (They should be speckled and have no green ends.) As these are blending, add the vanilla and carob powder, then the nut butter last. Try this sauce as a frosting on a banana cake or as a topping for waffles or pancakes.

LEMON SAUCE

Yield: Over 1½ cups

1 ½ c pineapple juice
1 T lemon juice
1–2 t honey
    1 t lemon rind OR ½ t lemon extract

⅛ t salt
¼ c coconut meal OR cashew meal
1 T starch

Bring 1 c of the pineapple juice to a boil. Blenderize the other ingredients in the remaining ½ c of juice, until smooth. Stir this into the boiling pineapple juice and stir-cook until well thickened. Chill or serve hot, as desired.

"CREAM CHEESE" SAUCE

Yield: about 1½ cups

1 ½ c water
¼ c raw cashew pieces
1 ½ T lemon juice
½ t salt

2 T barley flour, rice flour OR white flour
1 ½ t onion powder
¼ t EACH, celery salt and garlic powder
2 T brewer's yeast flakes

Blenderize ½ c of the water with all the other ingredients until very creamy. Add the rest of the water and stir-cook in a sauce pan until thick. For a variation, add ¼ chopped olives, ¼ c pimento or 2 T parsley. This sauce is good over cauliflower, broccoli, or boiled potatoes. It is also good as a spread.

SUNNY CHEE SAUCE
(good baked over macaroni)

Yield: about 2 cups

2 c canned tomatoes with juice
½ c raw sunflower seeds
2 T brewer's yeast flakes, (opt.)
1 T lemon juice

2 t honey (opt.)
⅛ t garlic powder
½ t EACH, onion powder and celery salt
½ t salt (omit if tomatoes are salted)

Boil tomatoes with sunflower seeds gently for 10 minutes. While hot, blenderize with the other ingredients until very smooth. Good over macaroni, vegetables, etc. as a cheese sauce.

CAROB-NUT ICING

Yield: over 1½ cups

1 c cold water
¼ c carob powder
1 t vanilla
¼ t salt

1½ T *Instant Clear Gel*
2 T honey OR 3 T *Sucanat*
½ c peanut butter OR tahini

Blenderize all but the nut butter until very creamy and thick. Place this in a bowl and whip in the nut butter with a wire whisk until very thick and smooth. Frost cake and chill for ½ hour to firm up frosting and moisten cake a little. Good on carob cake, muffins or toast.

SUNNY COTTAGE CHEESE

2 c hot water
1½ c raw sunflower seeds
¼ t onion powder (opt.)

1¼ t salt
⅓ c fresh lemon juice (1/2 c, if canned juice)

Blend all but lemon juice until coarsely ground (not until creamy). Bring this mixture to a boil, cover and simmer on low heat for 15 minutes. Stir once or twice during this time. Watch to prevent boil-over. Add lemon juice and stir through the curds. Cool, stir again and serve.

PIMENTO CREAM CHEESE

Yield: abut 2 cups

1 c tomato juice
¾ c cooked millet OR rice
1 T lemon juice
2 T brewer s yeast flakes

¼ c cooked pimento OR red bell pepper
¼ t EACH, onion powder and salt
½ c raw cashew pieces
⅛ t EACH, garlic powder and celery salt

Bring tomato juice and cooked millet to a boil in a covered saucepan. Blenderize this while hot, with all the other ingredients, until very smooth. Pour at once into a mold or container and cool **uncovered**. If you add another ¼ c of hot millet to the above, while blending, the cheese will slice, when cool. Only millet (not rice) will make the cheese firm enough to slice.

CASHEW SLICING CHEESE

1¼ c tomato juice
1½ c raw cashew nuts
¼ c yeast flakes
2½ t salt
2 t onion powder
½ c lemon juice

¼ t garlic powder
2 t paprika
⅛ t turmeric powder
1 c boiling water
6 T Unflavored *Emes* gelatin

Sprinkle the *Emes* gelatin into 1 c of boiling water (last two ingredients), and let set for 5 minutes. Combine all the other ingredients in the blender and blend until creamy. Add all of the gelatin mixture as you continue to blend. Pour cheese into a mold and chill to firm up. Slice, or if you wish to grate cheese, firm it up a little first in freezer.

PIZZA OR LASAGNA "CHEESE"
(or grilled cheese sandwiches)

Yield: 1½ cups

1 c cold water
⅓ c barley flour OR other flour
2 T lemon juice
¼ t garlic powder

½ c pimento OR ½ c cooked, drained
    tomatoes and ¼ t turmeric
⅔ c sunflower seeds OR nuts
½ t EACH, salt and onion powder
¼ c brewer's yeast flakes

Blenderize all the ingredients, but the flour, together until very creamy. Stir the flour in. It is ready now to use on a pizza or between the layers of lasagna. For grilled cheese sandwiches spread a generous layer of the cheese on slices of bread and bake at 400° F. for 25 minutes, approximately. Omit the flour, and it makes a nice cheese for baked macaroni. You may like to use a cake decorator to apply the cheese to the pizza, more artistically.

Spreads, Butters and Sandwich fillings

SPREADS, BUTTERS AND SANDWICH FILLINGS

Many people are turning from refined fats to natural butters. Avocados, nuts and seeds offer a variety of flavors. Of the nut butters on the market, sesame tahini (made from hulled sesame seeds), and peanut butter seem to be the most economical and versatile. Because of its rich, mild flavor, tahini may often be used in place of margarine. For a tasty, quick mayonnaise, add a little (1) lemon juice, (2) onion salt and (3) water (enough to make it creamy) to (4) tahini. Tahini and peanut butter may be purchased at bulk prices food buying clubs or health food distributors.

MILLET MARGARINE

Yield: 1 pint

2 c warm water
3 T raw millet grain
1 t unflavored *Emes* gelatin,
    dissolved in ¼ c hot water

2 T raw, peeled carrot chips (for color)
¼ c raw cashew nuts
1 t salt

Blenderize all but the *Emes* gelatin mix with 1 cup of the water, until finely ground. Add the rest of the water and stir-cook for 10 minutes, leaving lid on most of the time. May leave lid on a few minutes after heat is off, to unstick bottom of pan. Dissolve the *Emes* gelatin in the ¼ cup hot water. Blenderize the cooked mixture again and add *Emes* gelatin to it, blending until it is very smooth. Chill and serve.

BEAN SPREAD

1½ c cooked beans, thick and mashed (lima
    beans, black beans, navy beans,
    pinto beans, kidney beans, etc.)
½ t onion powder OR 2 T grated
    onion (opt.)

2 t lemon juice
½ c mayonnaise (see our recipes) OR ⅓
    c fine nutmeal and more lemon juice
2 T chopped parsley OR chives (opt.)
    salt, if needed

Mix all the ingredients together well. Use with lettuce leaves, etc. on an open-face sandwich or as filling in savory turnovers.

FRUIT BUTTERS AND JELLIES

Oven Fruit Butter—Put applesauce or other cooked, naturally sweet fruit, on a cookie sheet with raised sides, about ½ inch thick. Bake at about 300° F. until it becomes thick.

Dried Fruit Butters—Soak dried fruit with enough water or fruit juice to barely cover it, overnight **or** bring to a boil and leave covered for an hour. Place the soaked fruit and water or juice in the blender and blenderize until creamy. Some combinations we like are: orange juice and raisins, dates and apricots, pineapple (pieces and juice) and dates. You may like to add a **little** grated orange rind for a spicy flavor.

Fruit Jelly—Combine 1 c fruit juice (naturally sweet) and 1½ "*Minute Tapioca*" **or** 1½ T starch, and stir-cook until clear. Cool and serve. You may want a little more tapioca if this is not thick enough to suit you.

BLENDER NUT BUTTER

Yield: 1½ cups

1 c warm water
¼ t salt

Nuts (All kinds, except peanuts, may be raw)

Whirl the water in the blender while you add the nuts slowly, until the mixture becomes the consistency you desire. Chill first, or serve as it is. The butter will keep for several days if refrigerated.

CHICKEN-STYLE SANDWICH MEAT

Yield: 1 small cookie sheet

2½ c cold water
½ c raw cashew nuts
3 T food yeast flakes
2 t CHICKEN-STYLE SEASONING

¾ t onion salt
½ c soy flour
⅓ c cornmeal
½ c wheat flour OR barley flour

Blenderize ½ c of the water with the nuts and seasonings until very creamy (one full minute). While still blending, add the rest of the water and the flours. Pour onto a nonstick or greased cookie sheet with sides until the batter is about ½ inch thick on the pan. Bake at 375° F. for 35–45 minutes.

PEANUT SANDWICH MEAT

2½ c water
1 c lightly toasted, skinned peanuts
½ c fine cornmeal
1½ T food starch

½ t onion powder
¾ t salt
¼ t rubbed sage OR sweet basil

Blenderize all the ingredients together until creamy. Place in a covered baking dish or loaf pan. Bake 1 to 1¼ hours at 350° F. or until it starts to turn brown around the edges. Chill and slice for cold-cuts or serve hot. Or try adding ⅓ c additional water, pour the batter ½ inch thick on a cookie sheet with sides, and bake at 375° F. for about 45 minutes. Cut in squares when cool.

SAVORY SUNFLOWER SPREAD

Yield: about 2 cups

2 c hot water
1½ c raw sunflower seeds
1 t onion powder
¼ t garlic powder
2 T sesame tahini (opt.)

2 t soy sauce
3 T yeast flakes
⅓ t EACH celery salt and paprika
½ t salt
¼ c lemon juice

Blend the items in the left column only 30 seconds (coarse grind). Boil this gently in a saucepan for 15 minutes with lid on. Then stir in the flavorings in the right column, by hand, Chill or serve warm.

SUNFLOWER SANDWICH MEAT

Yield: 1 cookie sheet

2 c warm water
1⅓ c raw sunflower seeds
1 t onion salt (more if tomatoes
    are unsalted)

2 c pureed tomatoes
½ c soy flour
¾ c ww flour
½ c cornmeal

Blenderize the warm water with the sunflower seeds until creamy. Pour into a bowl and add the other ingredients. Mix thoroughly, then pour into a greased or nonstick cookie sheet with sides, until the batter is ½–¾ inch thick all over the pan. Bake at 375° F. for about 45 minutes. When cool, slice and serve.

PECAN SANDWICH MEAT

Yield: 1 pound

½ c soy flour
½ c cornmeal
½ c pecan meal
½ c gluten flour OR barley flour
1 t celery salt

⅓ t EACH, sage and thyme
½ t EACH, paprika and garlic powder
2 T soy sauce
1 t onion powder
1½ c cold water

Mix the dry ingredients in a bowl; then add the soy sauce and water. Mix very thoroughly. Place in a greased (a thin film of liquid lecithin works best for this), 20 oz. can. Cover with foil and make 2 air vents in the foil. Place the can in a kettle with water that reaches halfway up the sides of the can, and steam for 1½ hours **or** place in a pressure cooker, with water around it, and pressure cook for 45 minutes at 10 lbs pressure. Cool, slice and serve as sandwich meat. Gluten flour may be secured from most health food stores.

SANDWICH FILLING SUGGESTIONS

Sweet or Fruity Sandwiches:

1. A variety of nut or fruit butters are nice when used alone on bread, **"OAT BISCUITS"**, etc.

2. Peanut butter with slices of ripe banana is a favorite.

3. Fruit turnovers or baked sandwiches. Try combining chopped, dried fruit with a fresh fruit and wrap it in regular bread dough, in the shape you wish, and bake thoroughly. Serve cold.

4. Mix mayonnaise (without the vegetable seasonings) with equal parts of raisins and nuts.

5. Nut butter with flattened dates or figs, makes a very tasty and filling sandwich.

6. Peanut butter mixed with crushed pineapple

Savory Sandwiches:

1. Cooked tomatoes creamed together with peanut butter, onion salt, celery salt, etc.

2. Mashed beans, garbanzos or peas with mayonnaise or tomato paste and put together in a sandwich with bell pepper, cucumber, lettuce, sliced tomato or a thin slice of onion.

3. Sliced avocado and tomato with onion salt.

4. **"PIMENTO CREAM CHEESE"** and alfalfa sprouts or sliced radishes.

5. Sliced **"PEANUT SANDWICH MEAT"** with parsley sprigs and tomato slice.

6. Savory turnovers (baked sandwiches): **"BEAN SPREAD"** or cooked lentils seasoned with chopped celery, chopped onion, soy sauce and a little flour (or your own idea), placed on a round of rolled-out bread dough. Fold the round of dough over (forming a half circle), and crimp the edges. Allow to rise and bake like buns. Serve hot or cold.

7. Grated carrot and finely chopped peanuts with enough mayonnaise or nut butter to moisten and hold the carrot and peanuts together.

8. Open-face sandwiches with any of our patties, loaf slices, nutmeats or cold-cuts with mayonnaise and/or tomato slices, etc.

Salad Dressings

SALAD DRESSINGS

SUNNY SALAD DRESSING

Yield: over 2 cups

1 c raw sunflower seeds	¾ t salt
2 c hot water	¼ c fresh lemon juice (more, if reconstituted)
¾ t onion powder	

Blend all but the lemon juice until rather smooth. Bring to a boil in a saucepan. Cover and let simmer on **low** heat for 10 minutes. Stir once during this time. Then return to blender and blend with lemon juice until very creamy. Cool and stir before serving.

ALMOND MAYONNAISE

Yield: 1 quart

¾ c blanched almonds	½ t dill weed (OR to taste)
2 c warm water	1 c cooked, peeled white potato
2 t honey	1 t onion powder
1¼ t salt	½ c lemon juice

To blanch raw almonds, bring them to a boil in some water and let set aside for one minute, then cool a little and skins will pinch off easily. Blend the drained almonds and other ingredients, except for the dill and potato until finely ground, then add the potato slowly until mayonnaise is thick and creamy. Stir dill in by hand. Cool and serve.

CASHEW MAYONNAISE

Yield: over 2 cups

2 c water	1 t salt
½ c raw cashew nuts	1 t onion powder
¼ c raw sunflower seeds	3 T cornmeal
2 t honey	⅓ c fresh lemon juice (more, if reconstituted)

Bring 1 cup of the water to a boil, while you blend the other ingredients in the other cup of water (except for the lemon juice). Add this mixture to the boiling water slowly as it returns to a boil. Cover and simmer on low for 10 minutes. Stir every 3 minutes. Return to a clean blender and blend with the lemon juice until very creamy. Chill and serve. Nice over baked potatoes, salad or for sandwiches.

RICE MAYONNAISE

Yield: 1 full cup

½ c boiling water	¼ t EACH, salt and onion powder
¾ c well cooked brown rice	¼ t celery salt
2 t honey	2 T cashew pieces OR other light nuts
2 T lemon juice OR to taste	pinch of garlic powder

Blenderize all the ingredients together until very smooth. Chill and serve.

TOMATO FRENCH DRESSING

Yield: over 1 cup

1 c cooked tomatoes OR 1¼
   c raw tomatoes
¼ t onion powder
⅛ t EACH, celery salt and sweet basil

⅛ t salt
1–2 T lemon juice
1 t honey
   pinch of garlic powder

Blend all ingredients together until smooth. Good with tossed salad, lettuce wedges or stuffed tortillas.

SWEET AND SOUR DRESSING

Yield: 1 cup

½ c warm water
½ c cooked rice OR other leftover cereal
2 T lemon juice
1 T honey

⅛ t EACH, salt and onion powder
¼ t celery salt
1 T nutmeal (cashew or any other)

Blenderize until very creamy. Chill and serve, or serve as it is when freshly made.

GREEN DRESSING

Yield: about 1 cup

2–3 T lemon juice
½ c cold water
½–1 c fresh parsley, chopped OR green
   onion tops, chopped (packed)

2 t honey (opt.)
¼ t EACH, salt and celery salt
2 T cashew nuts OR sesame seed
⅓ c cooked rice OR millet

Blenderize all together until quite creamy. Let it set for at least 15 minutes before serving, so the flavors will blend. Good over tossed salad, plain boiled spaghetti or baked potatoes. It is not good if leftover for another day.

KETCHUP

Yield: ¾ cup

½ c tomato paste
2 T lemon juice
1 T honey

¼ t EACH, salt and onion powder
⅛ t garlic powder

Mix thoroughly with a fork in a small bowl. Good with bean burgers or pecan patties with mayonnaise on bread or with Oven **"FRENCH FRIES"**.

AVOCADO SALAD DRESSING

½ c ripe avocado
1–2 T lemon juice OR lime juice
   salt to taste

¼ c cold water OR enough to blend nicely
   a sprinkle EACH, of onion powder,
   garlic powder and celery salt

Place all the ingredients in the blender and whirl just enough to make it smooth. Good with tossed salad or bean burgers and alfalfa sprouts. It should be made shortly before mealtime.

Miscellaneous

MISCELLANEOUS RECIPES

HOMEMADE NOODLES

Yield: Enough for 1 quart of soup

⅓ c soy flour
⅔ c ww flour

¼ t **EACH, onion powder and salt**
¼ c **warm water**

Mix all together well. Roll out on a well floured counter top about ⅛ inch thick. Cut in small rounds, squares or in long strips. Drop into boiling soup, stew or beans and broth. Boil for 3 minutes, then turn the heat down and simmer for 20 minutes. Turn the heat off and leave alone for a half hour, for the best flavor.

OVEN "FRENCH FRIES"

Scrub potatoes and trim as necessary, but the jackets may be left on. Cut in strips **or** thin wedges with a French fry cutter or a knife. Put these in a bowl and toss with a generous sprinkle of onion powder, a little garlic powder and some salt. Mix thoroughly, so the seasoning will cover the potato strips evenly. Place these on a nonstick or lightly oiled pan. Bake at 450° F. for 35–45 minutes, depending on how crisp you like them. Serve hot.

CORN DUMPLINGS

Yield: for 6–8 cups broth

1 c **cornmeal**
⅓ c **sunflower seeds (raw)**
½ t **salt**

1 t **onion powder (opt.)**
2 T **tahini**
⅔ c **cold water**

Blenderize the cornmeal and sunflower seeds until very finely ground. Place in a bowl and stir in the salt, onion powder and tahini, until the tahini is thoroughly creamed into the dry ingredients. Add the water last of all and stir in well. Let set for a few minutes. Then push grape-size lumps of batter off the end of a spoon into boiling broth (of your choice). Simmer 15–20 minutes. See **"GARBANZOS AND DUMPLINGS"**. Also good in soupy black, red or pinto beans (which have first been cooked thoroughly and seasoned nicely).

GARBANZO OR SOY NUTS

Soak the beans or garbanzos overnight in plenty of water. They will double in volume. Rinse and place in a saucepan in these proportions:

1 c **soaked soybeans OR garbanzos**
1 t **salt**

1 c **water**

Bring this to a boil, then turn the heat off, but leave the lid on. Allow to set for 1 hour. Drain (but do **not** rinse), spread one layer thick on cookie sheets and bake at 300° F. or so, for 1¼ hours, or until just lightly browned and dry all the way through. Cool and place in airtight containers to preserve freshness. Keeps well for trips.

SCRAMBLED SOYBEANS

Serves 2–4

1¼ c soaked soybeans (soak ½ c (round)
    dry soybeans overnight)
1⅓ c cold water
2 t lemon juice

¾ t onion powder
2–3 t CHICKEN-STYLE SEASONING
⅛ t EACH turmeric and garlic powder
⅓ c quick rolled oats

Drain soaked soybeans, and measure the right amount. Blenderize all ingredients but the rolled oats until very creamy. Stir in the oats by hand. Cook in a nonstick, covered pan over low flame for 10 minutes. Turn but don't scramble yet. Bake for 15 minutes longer, then scramble gently with pancake turner. Be sure it is well done for best flavor. Serve hot.

SPROUTING SEEDS, BEANS AND GRAINS

You can sprout almost any whole, natural seed such as: Alfalfa, lentils, mung beans, soybeans, garbanzos, peas, sunflower seeds, wheat, rye, corn and oats. Check to be sure that the seeds are untreated. They may be obtained from a health food store. Sprouted radish seeds add a zesty flavor to salads. Sunflower seed sprouts add a rich flavor. Most persons prefer their legume sprouts after they have been steamed for a short time. Sprouting greatly reduces the cooking time required by legumes, even those usually requiring long cooking, such as soybeans and garbanzos.

To Sprout Seeds: (1) Put the seeds or grain in a glass jar and cover with water. Soak overnight. (2) In the morning, pour out the water, rinse the seeds and drain. (3) Until they are the right length to eat, rinse 2–3 times daily with a round screen or nylon netting over the mouth of the jar. After rinsing, leave the jar tilted so it will drain. Then roll jar to spread out seeds.

Soybeans and other **large** beans, lentils and grains are best when the sprouts are short, about ¼ inch long. Alfalfa and radish seeds can have longer sprouts.

1 T of alfalfa seed will fill a quart jar with sprouts. Use 2 T of radish seeds for a quart of sprouts. Use ¼ c of mung beans per quart and ½ c of sunflower seeds, wheat, rye, etc. Use 1 c of soybeans or other beans per quart of desired sprouts. For more information on sprouts, see the section on **"Sprouting Seeds"**.

UNFERMENTED DILL PICKLES

Yield: 1 quart

sm OR lengthwise cut cucumbers
1½ T salt
1 grape leaf (opt.)

¼ c lemon juice OR 2 t citric acid crystals
2 cloves garlic
2 T dill seed OR 2 heads fresh dill

Place the grape leaf in the bottom of the jar. Pack in the cucumbers and garlic tightly. Add the dill seed, salt and lemon juice on top. The cucumbers should not come above the neck of the jar. Fill the jars with very hot water up to the neck. Cap with a new canning lid and screw the ring on firmly, but not as tightly as you can. Boil the jars in a hot water bath for 10–15 minutes. (Start timing when the water bath starts boiling.) Cool the jars on a towel, check to be sure they are sealed, and store with the canned goods.

CINNAMON SUBSTITUTE MIX

3 parts ground coriander seed
¼ part ground cardamom (opt.)

1 part ground anise seed

Pulverize together with a mortar and pestle or in some other way. Store in an airtight container in a cool place.

CHICKEN STYLE SEASONING

1 c brewer's yeast flakes
2 T salt
2 T onion powder
1 T celery salt
1 T sugar (opt.)

½ t garlic powder
1 t sweet paprika
1 t Italian seasoning OR a mixture of sage,
    oregano and rosemary
1 ½ T dried parsley flakes (stir in last)

Blenderize all but the parsley flakes, very briefly. Stir in the parsley flakes and store in an airtight container in a cool place. Use as you would use "McKay's Chicken Style Seasoning".

SAFE SEASONINGS AND FLAVORINGS

Vegetable Seasonings:

Basil Leaf	Fennel Seed	Rosemary
Bay Leaf	Garlic	Saffron
Bell Pepper	Lemon Juice	Sage
Caraway Seed	Marjoram	Savory
Celery	Onions (of many kinds)	Tarragon
Chives	Oregano	Thyme
Coriander Leaf	Paprika (Spanish)	Tomato
Dill Seed & Weed	Parsley	

Fruit or Sweet Flavorings:

Carob Powder	Lemon Juice
Cardamom Seed	Lemon Rind
Coriander Seed	Mint
Extracts, Various Natural (almond, maple, lemon, etc.)	Orange Rind
	Nuts or Nut meal
Fruit Juice or Fruit Juice Concentrate	Various seeds
Honey (sparingly)	Vanilla

It is best to use only natural flavoring extracts such as, vanilla, orange, lemon, almond, etc. The imitation or artificial flavorings often contain aluminum and other questionable ingredients. Aluminum is under suspicion as a causative factor in Alzheimer's disease (early senility).

Index

Other books by TEACH Services, Inc.

Back To Basics *Dr. Arlene Taylor* .... $ 10.00
Timely tips for building bona fide boundaries and optimum self-esteem.

Caring Kitchen Recipes *Gloria Lawson* .... $ 12.95
Specializes in recipes for better health that features: whole grains, vegetarian, dairy-free and
nourishing dessert recipes.

Don't Drink Your Milk *Frank Oski, MD* .... $ 5.95
Dr. Oski, the head of Pediatrics at Johns Hopkins University School of Medicine, gives the frightening
new medical facts about the world's most overrated nutrient.

Earthly Life Of Jesus *Ken LeBrun* .... $ 19.95
Biblical accounts of each event in Christ's earthly life carefully arranged together from the KJV Bible.
Words of Jesus in red with full index.

Healing By God's Natural Methods *Al. Wolfsen* .... $ 4.95
Al. Wolfsen has taught hundreds of sick people how to use only simple, non-poisonous remedies.

His Name Is Wonderful *Leslie Hardinge* .... $ 10.98
In this book Dr. Hardinge has sought to bring out the highlights of twenty-three of the most common
names of God found in the Bible.

Hydrotherapy–Simple Treatments *Thomas/Dail* .... $ 8.95
Help your body overcome common diseases using hydrotherapy.

Incredible Edibles *Eriann Hullquist* .... $ 7.95
Some "health" meals taste bland, some are hard to make, others require strange or hard to find
ingredients. Eriann has developed a simple method of meal preparation where each recipe looks good
and tastes great.

Nutrition Workshop Guide *Eriann Hullquist* .... 10 for $ 9.95
Chalked full of nutritional recipes, as well as lots of helpful nutritional tips for special situations, such
as road trips, fast foods, etc.

Quick-n-Easy Natural Recipes *Lorrie Knutsen* .... $ 2.95
Every recipe has five or fewer ingredients and most take only minutes to prepare. Now you can enjoy
simple, natural recipes without the drudgery!

Returning Back To Eden *Betty-Ann Peters* .... $ 9.95
These recipes have been taste-tested by the world wide travelers that have visited the *Back to Eden
Restaurant & Bakery* in Minocqua, WI.

Studies in Daniel & Revelation *E.G. White* .... $ 4.95
Convenient pocketbook containing paraphrases of E. G. White's comments after each verse in the
books of Daniel & Revelation.

375 Meatless Recipes–CENTURY 21 *Ethel Nelson, MD* .... $ 7.95
This book will help you learn how to feed your family in such a way that they will enjoy eating the
foods that nutritionists tell us are an absolute must if we are going to make it into the twenty-first
century.

Victory On The Battlefield *Vaughn Allen* .... $ 7.95
In this book, the author draws on more than a decade of personal experience in ministering to "those
possessed by evil spirits."

To order any of the above titles, see your local bookstore.

However, if you are unable to locate any title, call 518/358-3652